Xing Yi Nei Gong
Xing Yi Health Maintenance and Internal Strength Development

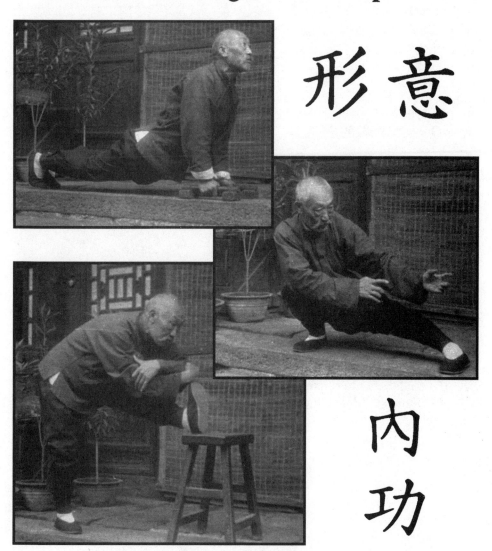

形 意

内 功

compiled and edited by
Dan Miller and Tim Cartmell

High View Publications, Pacific Grove, CA

Xing Yi Nei Gong
Xing Yi Health Maintenance and Internal Strength Development

Published by High View Publications
P.O. Box 51967
Pacific Grove, CA 93950

Printed in the United States of America

Disclaimer
   The author, translator, and publisher of the book are not responsible for any injury which may result from following the instructions contained herein.

   Before embarking on any of the physical activities described in this book, the reader should consult his or her physician for advice regarding their individual suitability for performing such activity.

Table of Contents

If the dan tian is lacking, the qi will not be sufficient. With insufficient qi, power will be inadequate. The five elements and the twelve forms will be empty. In this state, in defense one will be as a city surrounded by a dry moat, in attack, one will be like a strong soldier with a weak horse. One must practice diligently everyday. Sitting in meditation trying to become immortal will not cultivate the dan tian.

- from Dai Long Bang's Written Transmissions of Xin Yi Liu He Quan

Acknowledgements

First and foremost we would like to acknowledge Mr. Zhang Bao Yang and Mr. Wang Jin Yu for their willingness to share this information with the English speaking world. Additionally I would like to thank the translators who helped to translate interviews with Zhang Bao Yang and Wang Jin Yu when Tim Cartmell was not available. These individuals are: Bill Tucker, Huang Guo Qi, and Xu Yu Hong. Their skill in translation and patience during the long hours of interviews is greatly appreciated.

We would also like to thank Vince Black for proofreading and providing a forward to this book, Nancy Miller for her patience and proofreading, and Tim's wife Gu Feng Mei for her help in translating the written material.

Dedication

Wang Ji Wu (1891 - 1991)

王繼武

This book is dedicated to the memory of
Xing Yi Quan Master Wang Ji Wu.
His lifelong dedication to the martial and
healing arts and willingness to share
these arts openly with others should
serve as an inspiration and example for
future generations.

Preface

The material in this book is a culmination of nearly 100 years of experience in the art of Xing Yi Quan by Master Wang Ji Wu (王繼武), over 40 years of experience for each of Wang's students, Zhang Bao Yang (張寶楊), Wang Jin Yu (王金雨), and He Yu Qi (何宇岐), and over two years of collaboration between Wang's students, myself and Tim Cartmell. This material is straightforward, practical, easy to learn, and time tested.

Tim Cartmell and I first met Zhang Bao Yang on the sixth of October, 1992, in Beijing, China. We were at the home of Xie Pei Qi (解佩啓), a well known Ba Gua practitioner in Beijing. Xie had known we were coming and had invited some of his martial arts friends for the occasion. During our stay at Xie's home the focus of attention was Xie Pei Qi and his Ba Gua, however, I could not help but notice a distinguished looking elder gentleman sitting quietly in the corner observing the interview. Just before we were about to leave I asked to be introduced to the gentleman and found out he was Xing Yi Quan Master Zhang Bao Yang, President of the Beijing Xing Yi Quan Association. Zhang gave me his name card and I asked if we could visit with him in a few days. Zhang agreed and we arranged to meet him at his home on the eighth of October.

When Tim and I arrived at Zhang's home, two of his Xing Yi brothers, He Yu Qi and Pan Zhi Yuan (潘志源), were there with him. I asked Zhang and his classmates about their Xing Yi and they brought out some photographs of their teacher, Wang Ji Wu, and some written material they had compiled over the years. The old photographs fascinated me, especially a series of photos showing Wang Ji Wu performing a set of exercises. I asked about the photographs and Zhang explained that these were a set of sixteen health and body strengthening exercises that his teacher had studied over his lifetime of Xing Yi Quan practice and experience with Chinese medicine. His teacher had systematized the set and taught them to each of his Xing Yi Quan students as foundational training for Xing Yi. Zhang asked if I would like to see the set and allowed me to film him practicing all of the exercises. I was very impressed with the simplicity of the exercises and the thoroughness of the exercise set.

Zhang Bao Yang and his classmates were very open and generous during our first meeting. Zhang not only showed us the sixteen healing exercises and several of their Xing Yi Quan forms, but he allowed me to copy all of the photographs he had collected of his teacher and other Xing Yi Quan masters during his 40 years of studying the art. Tim and I were so impressed with Zhang and his knowledge of Xing Yi Quan that on October 11th we went back to visit him to conduct a more in-depth interview. During this interview we gathered more information about Wang Ji Wu and his Xing Yi Quan.

As impressed as Tim and I were about Zhang Bao Yang's knowledge of Xing Yi, we were both equally impressed with his personality and character. Tim commented many times about the clarity of Zhang's spoken word and his ability to express himself verbally. Tim said that it was obvious that Zhang was a man of high education. Zhang's home and his personal appearance were very neat and tidy, he was always energetic, had a very positive attitude, willingly answered any of our questions, and never had a bad thing to say about anyone else or any other Xing Yi system. While many Americans have a somewhat romantic view of the "scholarly boxer" and thus think that these are common qualities found in all of the old boxing masters, the fact is that Zhang Bao Yang is a rare individual in the boxing world in mainland China.

I left China at the end of October, however, Tim stayed in the mainland for several more weeks before returning to Taiwan. During his travels Tim ran across a book called *Shen Gong* (神功) which was written by Wang Ji Wu's son, Wang Lian Yi (王連義). One of the chapters contained the sixteen exercises which Zhang Bao Yang had shown us in Beijing. I began thinking about publishing a book which contained this exercise set and so I asked Tim to translate what was written in Wang Lian Yi's book.

I returned to Beijing in April 1993 and again visited with Zhang Bao Yang on several occasions. I told Zhang of my interest in publishing a book of his teacher's exercises and he thought that it would be a good idea. During this trip Zhang went through each of the sixteen exercises in great detail while Bill Tucker translated and I took notes. When I returned home I compiled all of the information and photographs that I had received from Zhang Bao Yang with the information Tim had translated from Wang Lian Yi's book to form the first rough draft of this book.

In September 1993, I returned to Beijing and showed the first rough draft of the book to Zhang. I found out that he and his classmates had also been busy preparing material for the book. They presented me with revised copies of the written material they had given me during my first visit and also gave me a very detailed written description of each of the exercises. Zhang Bao Yang and Wang Jin Yu were not particularly fond of the way Wang Ji Wu's son had presented the material in his book. They felt that his presentation was too esoteric and involved too much of the language of Chinese medicine. Zhang and Wang felt that the exercises should be explained in a very straightforward, useful manner and so they wanted me to use their explanations of the exercises. You will find that I have presented both Wang Lian Yi's material and Zhang Bao Yang and Wang Jin Yu's material in this book.

After returning to the United States, I sent the new material to Tim Cartmell to translate. The new material included the Xing Yi *Written Transmissions*, Explanations of the sixteen exercises, and historical information pertaining to Wang Ji Wu and Wang Fu Yuan. Additionally, the biographies of Wang's students were included.

Between November 1993 and March 1994, I put together all of the translated information, wrote a biography of Wang Ji Wu's Xing Yi lineage, added some material Tim had written about Xing Yi's standing practice, and printed a second rough draft of the book. In April 1994, Tim Cartmell and I went back to visit Zhang Bao Yang and Wang Jin Yu and showed them the second draft. Zhang and Wang were both pleased with the way the book was shaping up. During these meetings, we asked some more detailed questions about the exercises, the written transmissions, and Xing Yi's standing practice. Zhang Bao Yang also posed for all of the photographs presented in the sections on the sixteen exercises and the standing practice. Additionally, Zhang gave us a video tape he had prepared which contained all of the solo forms, two-person sets, weapons forms and supplemental exercises from their Xing Yi system. Included on this tape was also a power training set whereby Zhang performed Xing Yi's five elements with a long spear.

Since I wanted this book to represent all of the supplemental health and strength building exercises that a Xing Yi practitioner might practice in conjunction with the standard Xing Yi forms and two-person sets, I decided to add a chapter on the power training exercises with the long spear. After our trip to Beijing in April, I incorporated the new material with the draft version of the book and the result is what you now hold in your hands.

The exercises presented in this book are simple and functional. There is not anything "esoteric" or "mystical" about them. Like the art of Xing Yi itself, these exercises are direct, practical, and they produce results if practiced diligently.

In the Spring of 1993, Vince Black, Tim Cartmell, and I were interviewing a Xing Yi master in Taiwan. We had been asking questions of this gentleman for a couple of hours and as the interview came to a close Vince said, "Before we end this interview, are there any words of advice that you can give us regarding the practice of Xing Yi." The gentleman thought for a minute and then said, "You cannot be too smart and practice Xing Yi. Attainment of Xing Yi skill requires repetition of the same thing thousands of times. If you think too much you will not be content with repeating the same movements so many times. Practice hard, keep it simple, and don't be too smart!" This is the same as the Xing Yi Quan adage to "practice the plain without embellishment, practice simple movements until they are highly refined."

The same advice applies to the material presented in this book. For best results, the standing practice and health exercises should be practiced everyday before and after forms practice. Do not try to read too much into the exercises, keep them simple and practice everyday and the good results will naturally follow. We hope that you enjoy this book.

Dan Miller
Summer 1994
Pacific Grove, CA

Translator's Preface

by Tim Cartmell

There have been many books on Xing Yi Quan forms but very little written on training the basics and supplementary training. All martial arts include both forms training (*quan tao*) as well as supplementary power training (*lian gong*). There is a famous quote in the Chinese martial arts world which states, "If one practices martial forms without also training for power, in the end one will have achieved nothing." It is our hope that this book will be useful to those practitioners of Xing Yi Quan (or any other martial art) who are looking for traditional methods of power training to supplement their art. It should be noted that in addition to the potential increase in martial power that these exercises afford they are also excellent health building methods in their own right.

Why is it that the Chinese authors of books on Xing Yi Quan are willing to write extensively on the practice of boxing forms, but supplementary power training is usually mentioned in passing, if at all? The answer lies in the fact that boxing forms are useless unless the practitioner has the knowledge of how they are applied and the power to apply them. As simple and basic as some of the supplementary exercises may seem, they were generally kept "secret." The traditional concept of martial instruction was to drill a student in forms until the teacher was convinced of his sincerity and motives before the methods of power training and application were revealed. And these methods were usually concealed from the general public. Although in the modern world such ideas may seem a bit archaic, keeping in such information secret is still common among many teachers.

Dan Miller and I were fortunate enough to meet Zhang Bao Yang by chance. He had at one time been the head of the Beijing Xing Yi Quan Association and now serves as an advisor. Zhang was one of the top students of Wang Ji Wu, who in turn was one of the great Xing Yi Quan masters of this century. Zhang Bao Yang is one of those rare individuals who puts the promotion of his art above his own personal gain. He met with Dan and I several times and was completely open in sharing his knowledge with us. He taught us the set of sixteen exercises for health which his teacher had standardized and which formed the nucleus of their basic training. Although the method is referred to as a set of health building exercises, these movements are also the foundation of power training. In Xi An I came upon a copy of a book written by another of Wang Ji Wu's students (his son Wang Lian Yi) which included the sixteen health exercises and from which some of the information in this book is taken. But the above mentioned work left out many of the finer points which Zhang Bao Yang later included. Another of Wang Ji Wu's students, Wang Jin Yu was also most helpful in clarifying the finer points of training. The last time we visited Zhang, he also showed us advanced methods of power training with a long spear which should prove to be most useful to advanced practitioners of the art. In addition, there is a rather extensive section on the benefits and practice of stance keeping, another pillar of Xing Yi Quan basic training. I think this book is an important first step in presenting the "other side" of Xing Yi Quan training and I hope you will find the information included here useful to your own training.

Tim Cartmell
Summer 1994
Taipei, Taiwan

Foreword

by Vince Black

It is a privilege to write the forward to such an important piece of work on this lesser known aspect of traditional physical culture methods. This book very nearly stands alone in its originality as a contribution from a most senior master (and his students) of a traditional school of internal pugilism. This unique position is shared by few others, perhaps only Sun Lu Tang and Wang Zi Ping, due to the fact that few boxers attain such high level skills and knowledge in both martial arts and traditional Chinese medicine, as well as possessing the literary skill of writing, each of which requires years of study. Furthermore, acquiring expertise in these varied skills while trying to survive the tumultuous historical period of the last century in China was a monumental achievement in and of itself. The fact that we only now have it all consolidated in book form is a notion that requires more than a passing thought to appreciate. Wang Ji Wu and his students, in two generations spanning one hundred years, steadfastly persevered in their pursuit of a life of physical culture and medicine through famines, wars, military occupations, and political and social revolutions, none of which allows easily the uninterrupted pursuit of these arts. In spite of the discord and constant disruption in their lives, these inveterate boxers continued to practice their arts and this book is testimony not only to their personal achievement but to their willingness to share this knowledge openly with us.

Wang Ji Wu lived to 100 years of age remaining remarkably spry to very late in life. This impressive stretch of time allowed his world view to enrich itself several generations longer than most people; time to refine and focus on the points that really matter. His legacy was then carried on by his students Zhang Bao Yang, Wang Jin Yu, He Yu Qi, Wang Lian Yi, and others who have remained close and continue to follow his example. Mr. Zhang Bao Yang and his associates have worked together to produce this work in memory of their teacher and for the benefit of all those who value the traditional methods of physical cultivation of body, mind, and spirit.

In my own pursuit of Xing Yi Quan, spanning the last twenty years, I have researched many different expressions of Xing Yi from various sources. While each one may have their own stylistic difference, they all share the same essential principles of the art in varying degrees of emphasis. For my personal need I have selected several senior masters of Xing Yi from whom I draw to develop my personal art. My first "true teacher" in Xing Yi was Hsu Hong Chi of Taipei, Taiwan whose system I studied for ten years until his passing. The others from whom I gleaned valuable insights and methods are all men who have forty to fifty years experience in Xing Yi and all of these men, without exception, have high regard for their complementary or adjunctive exercises. While many of the exercises were the same or similar versions, some would be distinctly unique to that master and clearly reflective of his favorite personal techniques, or at least his own character and personal nature.

Supplementary exercises are often viewed as optional or nonessential. This is certainly a short sighted if not incorrect attitude. For the last ten years, I have traveled all over the U.S. and Canada teaching Xing Yi Quan for the North American Tang Shou Tao Association. In these efforts, working with study groups of internal boxers I have come to rely wholeheartedly on our multi-layered system of supplementary exercises to supplant the need of an ever present teacher which is almost never possible. On many occasions, I have had to respond to observers, more familiar with the generic martial expressions of Xing Yi proper, who would question the relationship of these exercises as they were unable to connect them specifically to the more well-known Xing Yi posturing. The perceptual problem results from the abstract nature of Xing Yi development in general and the tendency of human nature to attempt to relate seemingly familiar components from one school of thought to another and thereby short change the more sublime attributes of the other school. H.L. Mencken clearly grasped the problem when he said, "The critic, to interpret his artist, even understand his artist, must be able to get into the mind of his artist, he must feel and comprehend the vast pressure of the creative person."

Upon thorough examination, *Xing Yi Nei Gong* offers the reader many different perspectives from which to view the more profound developmental aspects of Xing Yi training for both the martial artists and for those interested in merely maintaining their optimum health far into the twilight of their years. Typical of Xing Yi methods, Wang Ji Wu's exercises are archetypically simple in design yet subtly profound in effect. This is quintessential Xing Yi.

If the fruit is any indication of the quality of the tree, then Mr. Zhang Bao Yang is proof positive of the efficacy of Wang Ji Wu's methods. I first met Mr. Zhang Bao Yang several years ago at his home in Beijing. We were waiting in his receiving room at his home when he arrived just before 11:00 pm. I was immediately impressed with the casual and easy manner with which he moved about the room offering us tea and food. Twenty minutes earlier we also had to climb the ten floors of stairs to his apartment and it seemed more taxing on us than on this man in his seventies. Shortly after his arrival from a long work day he received a couple from a neighboring apartment. It seemed the woman had thrown her back out and, nearly doubled over in pain, came to Mr. Zhang for emergency treatment. He graciously and energetically invited her to lie down on a makeshift table and proceeded to gently work on her. His methods were simple and few and he performed them effortlessly. Within twenty minutes she was up and smiling, thanking him repeatedly. He saw them off, walking them down the hall part way home, typical of Chinese etiquette, then returned to discuss his *Qi Gong*. He immediately took every opportunity and made every effort to see that we clearly understood he was not making any extraordinary claims about his *Qi* methods. He didn't approve of flim flam and abstruse methods of inexplicable phenomena. He regarded this kind of infatuation with the bizarre as unhealthy and possibly dishonest. Once we were able to assure him we were not interested in those types of performance, he openly and generously shared all that we were able to address in the time we had.

In subsequent visits and opportunities to view his abilities both teaching and performing his Xing Yi Nei Gong, Xing Yi Quan, and traditional medicine skills, it was clear that he is a true representative of the highest expression of Chinese physical culture. Nor is he the lone bastion of Wang Ji Wu's teachings, for several of his close associates in his kung fu family are equally refined in their comprehension of the arts of Xing Yi and traditional Chinese medicine as well as their own personal character.

Xing Yi Nei Gong is nothing short of another milestone in the development of internal boxing in the English speaking world. It is in fact providing that very element, so conspicuously missing in most Xing Yi programs, that is a specific focus on health maintenance and internal strength development through specific yet non-martial exercises. Some of the forms are performed with objective simplicity that can be viewed as a further abstraction of the slightly more subjective martial gesturing that lies at the heart of the system, which forms the root of certain martial stratagems. Other forms are less involved in active movements and more usefully regarded as static posturing in mimicry of natural elements, thereby capturing the psychological essence that lies at the heart of the natural power cultivated in the process. It is this multi-dimensional approach to exploring and developing the essence of our nature that I find Xing Yi a most fascinating art form.

This routine of Wang Ji Wu's has been developed, handed down, and further developed, organized and expounded upon by generations of Xing Yi practitioners of the highest order whose sole motivation was a lifelong love for the art of Xing Yi and whose hope and purpose was the preservation and proliferation of this magnificent art. As a method that targets ever higher levels of achievement, each exercise is built on a foundation developed by the previous exercise. Bearing this in mind, one will progress more quickly and with more complete results. This is not to dwell intellectually on these points but to simply appreciate their mutual relationship. To be able to see the thousand in the one, and the one in the thousand, one first has to manifest the principle.

For the purpose of providing a deeper and broader view of the relationship between these exercises and the Xing Yi system, several chapters have been added to offer more linkage between the supplemental training and the martial aspects of the art. Mr. Miller's and Mr. Cartmell's discussion of the basic concepts and structured analysis of the basic *san ti* posture of Xing Yi Quan offers many departure points from which to examine the various aspects of the basic essentials entailed in the Xing Yi foundation and manages to do so in a direct "just the facts" manner. A reading that any aspiring practitioner will find useful. The historical background information, along with the many rare photographs, and the material on the Xing Yi spear is an added bonus for those practitioners who seek further personal research material.

We owe a debt of thanks to Mr. Zhang Bao Yang, Mr. Wang Jin Yu, Mr. He Yu Qi, Mr. Wang Lian Yi, and all their brethren who shared in this contribution to all future generations of Xing Yi practitioners around the world. Fortunate we are to have been able to, through them, reach deeply into the past history of our art and come to know their teacher Mr. Wang Ji Wu.

Vince Black
Summer 1994
Tucson, Arizona

Chapter 1

Wang Ji Wu

and the lineage of his

Xing Yi Quan

Xing Yi Quan Master Wang Ji Wu (1891-1991)

Wang Ji Wu and the lineage of his Xing Yi Quan
by Dan Miller

Wang Ji Wu (王繼武), who was also known as Wang Zhong Gao (王鍾鎬), was a native of Shanxi Province, Yu Ci County, Dong Shan Village. He was born in 1891. His grandfather was a famous Chinese doctor and was considered incorruptible. Likewise, Wang's father was charitable and enthusiastically acted for the good of the community. In his youth, Wang Ji Wu studied in the village school and was a gifted student. He had a natural love of martial arts and studied what he could with the martial artists of his village. He was a student by day and the watchman of a gourd patch at night, which left plenty of time for martial arts practice while at work. During a lifetime of study, Wang became an expert of martial arts (including *qi gong* - 氣功) and Chinese Medicine (including osteopathy). Because of his deep understanding of both the martial and medical arts, his level of attainment in both was very high. He led a stable life, placing justice above material gains, and took pleasure in helping others. Because of this, he was much respected and admired by his friends and family.

Wang Ji Wu's Xing Yi lineage

At sixteen years of age, Wang Ji Wu moved to the city of Tai Yuan in Shanxi Province to apprentice in business. Here, when he was eighteen years of age, he was introduced to Wang Fu Yuan (王福元), a top student of the famed Xing Yi Quan master Liu Qi Lan (劉奇蘭).

Xing Yi Quan (形意拳) was created at the end of the Ming Dynasty by Ji Long Feng (姬隆風 - also known as Ji Ji Ke - 姬際可) of Shanxi Province. In succeeding generations the art spread throughout Shanxi, Hebei, and Henan provinces and subsequently to the rest of the world. Wang Ji Wu's Xing Yi Quan lineage is well known to

A young Wang Ji Wu

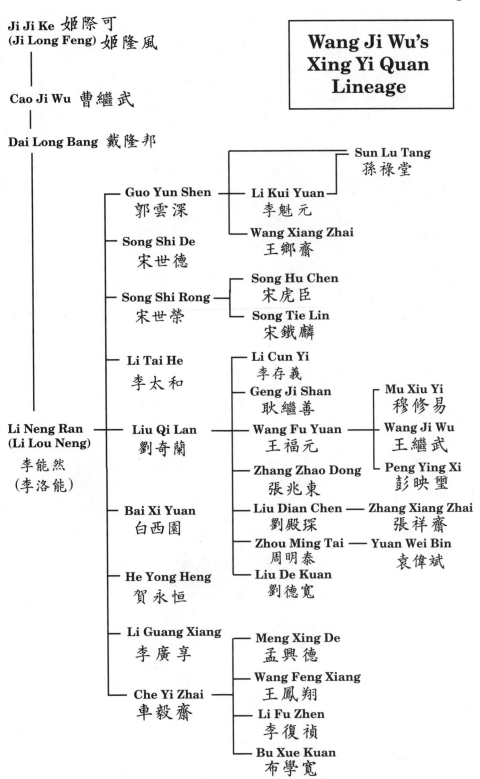

Ji Ji Ke 姬際可
(Ji Long Feng) 姬隆風

Cao Ji Wu 曹繼武

Dai Long Bang 戴隆邦

Wang Ji Wu's Xing Yi Quan Lineage

Li Neng Ran
(Li Lou Neng)
李能然
(李洛能)

Guo Yun Shen 郭雲深
Song Shi De 宋世德
Song Shi Rong 宋世榮
Li Tai He 李太和
Liu Qi Lan 劉奇蘭
Bai Xi Yuan 白西園
He Yong Heng 賀永恒
Li Guang Xiang 李廣享
Che Yi Zhai 車毅齋

Sun Lu Tang 孫祿堂
Li Kui Yuan 李魁元
Wang Xiang Zhai 王鄉齋
Song Hu Chen 宋虎臣
Song Tie Lin 宋鐵麟
Li Cun Yi 李存義
Geng Ji Shan 耿繼善
Wang Fu Yuan 王福元
Zhang Zhao Dong 張兆東
Liu Dian Chen 劉殿琛
Zhou Ming Tai 周明泰
Liu De Kuan 劉德寬
Meng Xing De 孟興德
Wang Feng Xiang 王鳳翔
Li Fu Zhen 李復禎
Bu Xue Kuan 布學寬

Mu Xiu Yi 穆修易
Wang Ji Wu 王繼武
Peng Ying Xi 彭映璽
Zhang Xiang Zhai 張祥齋
Yuan Wei Bin 袁偉斌

Note: This lineage listing is by no means all inclusive. The names listed here are only those mentioned elsewhere in this book.

Wang Ji Wu (left - age 63) sits with two of his Xing Yi Quan friends, Ma Yu Tang (center - age 82) and Zhang Xiang Zhai (nicknamed the "Iron Lohan" - age 80). This picture was taken in 1954. Wang Ji Wu lived to be 100 years old, Ma Yu Tang died at 87, and Zhang Xiang Zhai lived to be 96.

those who are familiar with the history of Xing Yi Quan. He was a seventh generation inheritor of the style of Xing Yi Quan which originated with Ji Ji Ke (also known as Ji Long Feng). Ji Ji Ke passed his art to Cao Ji Wu who passed it to Dai Long Bang, who in turn passed it to Li Neng Ran (also known as Li Lou Neng). Li Neng Ran taught Liu Qi Lan, who taught Wang Ji Wu's teacher, Wang Fu Yuan. Thus Wang Ji Wu was of the seventh generation of Ji Ji Ke's Xing Yi Quan (see detailed lineage chart on the previous page).

Dai Style Xing Yi Quan (戴式形意拳)

The style of Xing Yi Quan which Wang Ji Wu taught and practiced is known as the Dai style of Xing Yi Quan (originally called *Liu He Xin Yi Quan* 六合心意拳) because it descended from Cao Ji Wu's student, Dai Long Bang.

Dai Long Bang was born in the beginning of Qing dynasty in Shanxi Province, Qi County. His family had two sons. He had an older brother named Dai Ling Bang (戴陵邦). They both had liked practicing martial arts since they were young. As small boys, the two brothers practiced mimicing fighting movements with sticks and other objects they found and enjoyed practicing kicking, stretching, lifting weights, and throwing sand bags. By the time Dai Long Bang was in his teens his arms were very strong. One day in the village a millstone fell and no one could move it. Dai approached the stone, squatted down, picked it up and put it back were it belonged. Soon Dai became famous for his strength. They called him "two donkey" Dai because he was so strong.

One year in the summer it rained continuously for over ten days and the street

4

out in front of their shop became like a river. Someone was delivering goods in a wagon and the wheels of the wagon got caught in the mud. Four or five workers couldn't move the wagon out of the mud. Dai said, "Let me try." With one breath and a shove he pushed the wagon out of the mud. The people watching started calling him "strong man" Dai.

After Dai lifted the wagon, he heard a laughing voice behind him saying, "Ha, you are really a strong man!" He turned around and saw an old man standing there. Dai felt that the man had a special look about him. Dai said, "I can tell by your accent you are from Qi County. However, I don't think I have ever seen you before." Dai asked him who he was and the man said that his name was Cao Ji Wu. He had been traveling for years and was now on his way home. Dai invited him in for a rest.

As Dai and Cao were walking through the courtyard, they passed by a tree. Cao acted as if he was tripped by a tree root and looked as if he was going to fall forward. Dai grabbed Cao around the waist in an attempt to pull him up before he fell to the ground. No matter how hard he tried, Dai could not pull him up. It was as if Cao had roots in the ground. Cao finally stood up, laughed and said, "Ha, strong man, where is your strength now?" Dai knew that Cao was a man of uncommon skill and bowed before him to ask to become his student.

The next day Cao said he was leaving to go back to the countryside. Dai begged him to stay. Cao agreed to stay for a few days. Dai fed him well and did everything for him. Cao, enjoying this arrangement and in no hurry to get home, stayed with Dai for three months. Everyday Dai asked if Cao would teach him and Cao refused.

Dai and Cao slept in the same room and one night Dai woke up and discovered Cao was gone. The next few nights Dai pretended he was asleep and each night he saw Cao sneaking out as soon as he thought Dai had fallen asleep. Dai pretended to fall asleep again the next night and after Cao had left, he went out to see what Cao was doing. When Cao reached the wall around the courtyard in front of Dai's home he easily leapt over it. The wall was high so Dai had to climb his way over. Cao went out into a clearing and began to practice his martial arts. His movement was fast, accurate and vicious. Dai was so impressed that he could not contain himself as he cried out in amazement. Cao turned around and seeing Dai said, "I am old now and can't move so well, please do not laugh at me for doing martial arts this way.

They went back to have tea. Cao said that since Dai had seen him, he wouldn't hide the truth from him anymore. He said "I was a inner door student of Ji Ji Ke for ten years." Cao revealed that in the scholarly exams he had reached the first level and in the martial examinations he had placed second. The Emperor gave him the position as the chief constable of the county in Shanxi and then later he became the governor. He retained his public position for over ten years but became tired of the corruption. After resigning his position, he left and traveled around the country to meet people.

Cao found Dai to be very sincere and trustworthy. He had stayed at Dai's home for three months without accepting him as a disciple in order to test his character. During this time, he saw that Dai was honest and upright. Dai again knelt and asked to be accepted as a student and this time Cao agreed.

After agreeing to accept Dai as a student, Cao told Dai about his own teacher. At the end of the Ming Dynasty there was a man from Yong Ji County, Shanxi

Province. He was a man of great ability named Ji Ji Ke. He was also known as Ji Long Feng. He took the imperial exams, passed the test with high marks and became an official in Shaanxi. He was upright and honest and spoke the truth. Because of his honesty, he upset some of his corrupt superiors and they forced him out of office. After leaving office he then traveled around China.

On one occasion Ji was in Xi An visiting a friend. It was getting dark and started to rain so he ran into a Jing Wu temple. It was an old and dilapidated place. He saw a statue of Yue Fei (岳飛) in the temple and realized it was a temple dedicated to the memory of Yue Fei. Ji looked closely at the statue and noticed that it was cracked. He could see something inside the crack and so he took his sword and chipped away around the crack. Inside he found a manuscript called *Yue Fei's Six Harmony Xin Yi Boxing Manual*. He was very happy because everyone knew about Yue Fei's family of martial arts but between the time Yue Fei was alive and Ji Ji Ke's time, the art had been lost. He followed the manual and practiced hard. He later went back to his home in Shanxi province. He copied the book onto nice paper to preserve it. Ji later met and accepted Cao Ji Wu as his disciple.*

Dai Long Bang asked Cao what was special about Xing Yi. Cao said that it was also called *Liu He Xin Yi Quan* (Six Harmony Xin Yi Boxing). There are twelve forms and twelve styles, three turnings and three returnings, methods of attacking and methods of defending. All of these methods are together in one body. The movements are very agile and adroit and can change very quickly. Even if you are walking in pitch black night and there is a slight breeze, you will react and turn with the breeze.

Dai became very excited and wanted to start learning immediately. Cao felt Dai's shoulders and said, "Although your shoulders are like steel and your *dan tian* is hard, there is nothing inside." He continued, "You have the hard shell of a strong man, but no internal substance." Dai replied, "I don't understand what you mean." Cao said, "The martial arts you have practiced in the past have been practiced incorrectly. Because you have lifted heavy weights, your body is very hard and tight. With this type of body, there is no way you can practice Xing Yi." Dai Long Bang got nervous and said, "Does this mean that I have ruined myself and cannot ever practice Xing Yi." Cao said that it was not too late and taught Dai exercises such as the tiger step, how to squat like a monkey, and *San Ti Shi* (trinity standing posture), in order to open up his body inside and cultivate his *qi*.

After a few days, Cao felt that Dai was practicing the movements correctly and said "I am leaving you now. Practice these movements seriously for a year and then I will come back and see how you've done. I will then judge whether or not you are ready to learn Xing Yi." A year later, Dai went out to practice one day and saw an old man on the ground on his hands and knees. He went out to help the old man get up. He couldn't lift the man's body, but could lift his arm. The man turned around and Dai saw that it was Cao Ji Wu. Cao said, "I see you have been practicing, you can now lift up my arm. I think you are now ready to start learning Xing Yi."

---

* The true origin of Ji Ji Ke's Xing Yi Quan is unknown. This story about him finding Yue Fei's manual is the popular version of Xing Yi Quan's origin, however, it cannot be verified. Some versions of this story say he found Yue Fei's manual in a cave, others say it was given to him by a stranger and the story above says he found it in a temple. Others say that Ji Ji Ke originated Xing Yi himself based on the movements of the spear. The truth will never be known.

This picture was taken in the late Qing Dynasty when Guo Yun Shen went to Taigu, Shanxi Province to visit Che Yi Zhai. The two individuals seated in the middle are Che Yi Zhai (left) and Guo Yun Shen (right). The rest of the people in the photograph are Che Yi Zhai's students. The two individuals practicing in front are Li Fu Zhen (left) and Fan Yong Qing (right). The people standing in the back (from left) are: San Guang Shi Fu, Guo Yu Shan, Wang Feng Xiang, Liu Jian (standing in the middle), Wang Zhi Gui, Meng Lian Sheng, and Wu Jie

Cao taught Dai some new exercises and then left again to allow him time to practice on his own. This went on for eight years. Cao showed up at Dai's home, taught him some new exercises and forms, stayed long enough to ensure that Dai was performing the exercises correctly and then left for one year. One day, after eight years, Cao came back with some ropes made of cow tendons and tied them around Dai's waist. Dai laid on the ground and Cao said, " I am going to grab the rope and lift you off the ground. The last time you lifted me, it is now my turn to lift you." Cao lifted and the rope broke. Cao said, "This rope broke not because you don't have *gong fu* or because I am too weak. It is that the rope is too weak for both of us. We are now even."

Dai jumped up and said, "How could I ever begin to compare myself to my master." Cao said, "For a good student, I can tell them 'one' and they can figure out 'two.' You are now at the level where I tell you 'one' and you can count to ten on your own. You are the inheritor of my style." Cao then gave Dai his sword. He said, "You can never be complacent. If you practice one day you gain one day. If you miss one day, then you loose ten days. Remember, always be discriminating in whom you teach."

The next morning Dai woke up and Cao was gone. He waited for him to return for ten years and then went searching for him, but Cao was never found. Dai later found out that Cao went to Jung Nan mountain, near Xian, to cultivate himself and he died there. Dai Long Bang became the inheritor of the style and practiced diligently. He came up with new things from the old things. Xing Yi Quan entered a new phase of development with him, so he is considered to be the founder of this style and it is now called "Dai Family Xing Yi Quan." Dai Long Bang was one of the most respected historical figures in martial arts in China, he lived to be 90 years old. Dai's most famous students were his son, Dai Wen Jun, his nephew, Dai Wen Xiong, and Li Neng Ran. The *Written Transmissions* which appear in Chapter 2 of this book were handed down from Dai Long Bang and his student Li Neng Ran.

Li Neng Ran (李能然)

The majority of the Northern style Xing Yi Quan that is practiced around the world today can be traced directly to Dai Long Bang's student, Li Neng Ran (also known as Li Lou Neng). Li Neng Ran was from Shen County in Hebei Province. When he was 37 he went to Shanxi, Qi County and studied Xing Yi from Dai Long Bang and later with Dai's nephew Dai Wen Xiong (戴文雄). He studied for years and became very good at Xing Yi and then taught martial arts to bodyguards. Li was employed by the owner of a bodyguard service in Tai Gu, Shanxi Province for a number of years and began teaching Xing Yi Quan in Tai Gu. His first Xing Yi Quan disciple was Che Yi Zhai.

Since Li Neng Ran worked for a bodyguard service, he frequently traveled and taught students in various parts of Shanxi and Hebei. Later, he moved back to his home in Shen County, Hebei Province and taught students there. Two of his most famous students, Liu Qi Lan and Guo Yun Shen were from Shen County. Li Neng Ran had several students who became very well known for their Xing Yi Quan. Among them were Che Yi Zhai, Guo Yun Shen, Liu Qi Lan, Bai Xi Yuan, Song Shi Rong, Song Shi De and his son, Li Tai He. Li's students who did the most to propagate his art were Che Yi Zhai, Song Shi Rong, Liu Qi Lan and Guo Yun Shen. Liu Qi Lan and Guo Yun Shen taught Li Neng Ran's Xing Yi in Shen

County, Hebei Province. Che Yi Zhai and Song Shi Rong taught in Shanxi Province.

Li Neng Ran could possibly be called the "father" of the Northern styles of Xing Yi Quan. Li is known for refining and adding to what Dai Long Bang had taught him. Li is credited with developing many of the two-person forms, such as *Wu Xing Sheng Ke* (五行生克) and *Ai Shen Pao** (挨身炮), now practiced by Xing Yi practitioners in northern China. Some say that he worked out these two-person sets with his top student Che Yi Zhai.

Li Neng Ran is also thought to have changed some of the animal styles and added new ones. Additionally, it is thought that Li came up with the principles of keeping the elbows close to the ribs and keeping the fists in front of the heart. His idea was that the practitioner should use the body and steps in striking more than

Che Yi Zhai (left) with Guo Yun Shen in Tai Gu, Shanxi.

using the extension of the arms as in the old style of Xing Yi.

Li Neng Ran created many new ideas and forms to add to the art he learned from his teacher. He was a great innovator and is responsible for coming up with many of the fundamental principles of Xing Yi Quan practice.

Che Yi Zhai (車毅齋)

Che Yi Zhai, also known as Che Yong Hong (車永宏), was the second child in his family and people called him "Che number two." He was born in 1833 in Tai Gu City, Shanxi Province, Tao Yuan Bao Village. When he was young his family was very poor. From the time he was a small boy he followed his father to do manual labor. When he was ten he was sent to a rich family's ranch to work as a shepherd.

Che was often beaten and cursed at by his employer. One time he lost a female sheep and the family beat him with a stick, made his father pay for the sheep and then fired him. Only after his father begged for his job was he accepted back.

---

*Ai Shen Pao, or "close body pounding," is also commonly known as *An Shen Pao* (安身炮) or "stable body pounding." Xing Yi practitioners from Shanxi Province say that the original name of this form was *Ai Shen Pao*, however, since many Xing Yi men were illiterate, somewhere along the line the name was mistakenly changed. While most practitioners in Hebei Province now call this form *An Shen Pao* many of the practitioners in Shanxi Province still call it *Ai Shen Pao*. Since this form was originally developed to practice close-in fighting strategies *Ai Shen Pao* is the name that makes more sense.

9

Che Yi Zhai   **Song Shi Rong**

However, this incident left an impression on him about bullies and he vowed to study martial arts.

Everyday Che would carry a young calf in his arms while he exercised in order to make himself stronger. One day he was wrestling with a cow and threw it. His employer saw him and took a switch to beat him. Che grabbed the switch and snapped it in half, threw it on the ground and quit his job. He then went to another wealthy family in Tai Gu and got a job driving an ox cart. His employer's name was Wu Bo Nian (武柏年). At that time Tai Gu had the nickname of "gold" Tai Gu because there were a lot of rich people living there.

The streets of Tai Gu were narrow and there was not enough room for two carts to pass each other in the alleys. There was a rule that if two carts met on a street, the person of higher social standing got to go first. One day Che was taking his employer through an alley. They were almost to the end of the alley when the wealthiest man in the county approached with his cart. Che said, "Can you just back up a few feet and let me go through." Che's employer whacked Che with a stick and then got out and apologized to the other man because Che had not followed the proper etiquette. Che was shocked at the unfairness of it all and wanted to practice the martial arts with even stronger resolve.

One day Che was at home with his boss. His boss' nephew came over and saw that Che was very strong. His nephew's name was Wu Hong Pu (武鴻圖) and was a Shaolin student of a monk name Wang Chang Dong (王昌東). Che was smart and saw the opportunity to practice martial arts and asked Wu Hong Pu if he would teach him. Wu accepted Che as a student. Che practiced with Wu Hong Pu for five years.

Wu Hong Pu recognized that Che Yi Zhai had a lot of potential and took him to his teacher. Che began practicing with Wang Chang Dong and his skill improved greatly. One day his boss, Wu Bo Nian, told Che Yi Zhai that if he could become very skilled at martial arts, he could be his bodyguard and take care of his house. Wu Bo Nian happened to have a friend named Meng and the Meng family told him that they had a really good martial artist who taught the employees of their bodyguard service. They suggested to Wu that Che could come learn from him. The teacher of their bodyguard service happened to be Xing Yi Quan master Li Neng Ran.

When Li Neng Ran saw how hard Che practiced, he agreed to teach him. The Wu family brought Li to their house and hired him to teach Che Yi Zhai. Li often had to go out to work as a bodyguard and escort convoys, however, he was back in Tai Gu five or six times a year between trips. Whenever he was in Tai Gu, he taught Che. Because Li wasn't there a lot, Che also went back to his old Shaolin teacher to learn more. When Li heard about this, he was not angry. He was touched by Che's enthusiasm. Because Che was so enthusiastic, Li took him to meet Dai Long Bang's nephew Dai Wen Xiong in Shanxi Province, Qi county. Dai had also been a bodyguard, but was now retired. Che went to study with Dai every chance he got. Dai Wen Xiong was already quite old by then and didn't accept new students, but Li Lou Neng, who was one of his best students, talked him into accepting Che. Dai's home was 20 miles from where Che lived and Che walked there almost everyday to practice.

Dai Wen Xiong often said, of my system I have two inheritors, Li Neng Ran and Che Yi Zhai. He taught everything to Che. He taught Che that martial arts were to protect yourself and others and one should always be very selective in accepting students. Before Dai Wen Xiong died at the age of 96, he gave Che his manual of Xing Yi martial arts. Because Che studied with Li and Dai, he studied the whole breadth of the Xing Yi art and came to understand the pure essence. He became a famous martial artist, but he never bullied people. When people came to challenge him, he did not hurt them. He would entice them into emptiness and use their own force against them.

Around the turn of the century the Chinese people were very weak. A corrupt government, foreign invasion, opium addiction, and years of bad harvest had beaten them down. Che felt like he wanted to help strengthen the country and the reputation of the Chinese people. In 1888 in the Japanese concession in Tianjin, a sword contest was held. The Japanese representative had already beaten several famous swordsmen from Tianjin and Beijing. He was a very good swordsman, but was also overly arrogant. He loved to make wild claims about how good he was in front of the Chinese. Che heard about the challenge and traveled to Tianjin. He got there in the morning, went directly to the contest place and jumped up on the platform. Some people in the audience recognized him and word quickly spread that the famous Xing Yi master Che Yi Zhai was there. The crowd began clapping wildly. The Japanese swordsman noticed from the way Che jumped on the stage that he was skilled and so he stepped up proudly, trying to hide his fear. The Japanese man said, "You must not be afraid of death if you have come to challenge me."

The two men squared off with swords and the Japanese man attacked first. Che allowed the Japanese martial artist to back him to the edge of the platform and then Che suddenly whirled around and was behind his opponent. The Japanese man was now on the edge of the stage. Che poked him with his sword on the shoulder and his opponent was teetering on the edge. Instead of pushing

Li Fu Zhen   **Song Tie Lin**

him off or stabbing him, Che just backed up and said, "A-ha."

Che then started making blindingly fast movements with his sword and cut his opponent's wrist. The Japanese opponent lost his sword and acknowledged defeat. After that fight, Che became famous all over China. The government awarded him the highest level of martial skill, recognizing him for his achievement.

In 1900, during the Boxer Rebellion, the "boxers" started their revolt in Tai Gu and asked Che to teach them martial arts. On July 31, 1900 they attacked an American church. Che was to old to go, but he sent two of his students, Meng Xing De (孟興德) and Wang Feng Xiang (王鳳翔) and they were the first to go in. They killed a group of American missionaries and felt it was a great honor for China. Later, after the boxers lost the war, the famous Xing Yi instructor Li Cun Yi (李存義), who had fought in the rebellion and killed many foreigners, fled Beijing because the foreigners were after him. He went to Tai Gu and Che Yi Zhai helped hide him. Che also sent his student Li Fu Zhen (李復禎) to stay with Li for protection. The foreigners had put a price on Li's head, so many corrupt Chinese martial artists were after him. Li Fu Zhen went and killed them all. Li Fu Zhen was a servant at Wu Bo Nian's home and was Che Yi Zhai's first student.

During Li Cun Yi's stay in Tai Gu he also spent more than 20 days practicing Xing Yi in Song Shi Rong's courtyard with Song's young student and nephew Song Tie Lin. Later Song Tie Lin (宋鐵麟) said that he and Li compared five elements, twelve animals and practiced *Ai Shen Pao* together. Song Tie Lin died in 1975 at the age of 94.

In 1856, Xing Yi Quan came to Tai Gu with Li Lou Neng. Li Lou Neng's first Xing Yi disciple was Che Yi Zhai, the second was He Yong Hong (nicknamed

Zhang Zhao Dong   **Li Cun Yi**

"divine legs"), next was Li Guang Xiang, Song Shi Rong and his brother Song Shi De. These were his five famous students in Tai Gu who later became known as the "five stars meeting in Tai Gu." These five students later got together with Che Yi Zhai and called their style the Che family Xing Yi Quan.

The last time that Li Lou Neng went to Tai Gu he was 79 years old and could still perform the *Ai Shen Pao* form with Che Yi Zhai. As they were practicing, Li noticed that Che had changed some things. Li was surprised. Che said, "Forgive me for changing your form." Li told Che that he had changed it for the better.

Guo Yun Shen (郭雲深)

Guo Yun Shen had studied Xing Yi Quan with Li Neng Ran in Shen County, Hebei Province. Guo loved to fight when he was young. When he first approached Li Neng Ran wanting to learn Xing Yi Quan, Li would not teach him because Guo was of such a violent nature. Li told Guo that unless he could change his character, he would never teach him martial arts. Guo got a job as a servant near Li's home and would secretly watch Li and his students practice Xing Yi. Guo practiced *Beng quan* (崩拳 - smashing fist) on his own for three years. One day Li Neng Ran saw Guo practicing *beng quan* and noticed that Guo was very good at it already. Li realized that Guo was sincere about learning Xing Yi Quan so he then agreed to teach him.

After Guo had studied with Li for a few years he got a job as a bounty hunter. The law of the day said that a bounty hunter was allowed to catch criminals and bring them in, however, the criminals had to be brought in alive. On one occasion, Guo was hunting a bandit who was terrorizing travelers along a

Geng Ji Shan   **Peng Ying Xi**

frequently traveled road. Guo found the bandit he was pursuing while the bandit was engaged in a fight with a local escort service. Guo joined the battle and captured the bandit, however, after he had captured him, the bandit pulled out a concealed weapon and tried to kill Guo. Guo hit the man and killed him. Recognizing that he had done wrong, Guo turned himself in to the authorities. The penalty for such a crime was death, however, the local magistrate's advisors begged him to consider not executing Guo because he was a rare talent in the martial arts. Instead of execution, the magistrate sentenced Guo to three years in prison. While in prison Guo was manacled, however, he continued to practice his Xing Yi Quan. When he came out of prison his skill was higher than when he had entered.

While in prison, Guo had developed what became known as *ban bu beng quan* (半步崩拳 - half step smashing fist) and became so famous for the power he developed with this special punch that people said that his "half step smashing fist could beat all under heaven." After being released from prison, Guo went to visit the escort service doing business in the area where the bandit he had killed had operated. He told them that ever since he had killed the bandit, the road was clear and their job had become easy. He told the escort service that they owed him money because of the work he had done for them. Because of his martial arts skill, they did not want to quarrel with him so they gave him some money. However, Guo would periodically come back for more money and the escort service got tired of it. Instead of confronting Guo directly, they sent a letter to Guo's teacher Li Neng Ran.

Li Neng Ran called Guo back home and told him that he shouldn't bother the escort service any more. Li also said, "Plus, your *gong fu* is not nearly as good as you think it is. Your skill does not come close to that of your older brother Che Yi Zhai." In telling Guo this, Li wanted to teach him two lessons. The first was that he should not be so arrogant because no matter how good someone gets, there is always someone better. The second reason was to try and bring him back to complete his Xing Yi training. After Guo learned the five fists of Xing Yi, he did not want to study anything else. He was so good at applying the five fists that he never lost a fight, therefore, he concluded that he did not need to learn anything else. Li had encouraged Guo to study Xing Yi Quan's subsequent forms and two-person sets after he had learned the five fists, but Guo thought it was a bother and left Li before his Xing Yi training was complete.

Upon hearing that his teacher thought that Che Yi Zhai's skill was better than his, Guo became angry and went to Shanxi Province to find Che Yi Zhai and challenge him. When Guo arrived at Che's home, Che was happy to see him and said "Little brother, I am glad you have come to visit! Let's have something to eat." Guo said, "No, I came here to fight." Che tried to talk Guo out of fighting, but Guo persisted and thus Che was left without a choice. Guo tried to use his famous *beng quan* over and over. Che kept backing away from Guo's strikes and then quickly turned to the side as Guo struck again and executed *pi quan* (劈拳 - splitting fist). Che held the strike, stopping inches from Guo's head. Realizing that Che had got the best of him, Guo stopped and said, "It is just as our teacher has said, you are better then I." Following this incident Guo never bothered the escort company again and he went back to Li Neng Ran in order to complete his Xing Yi Quan training.

Liu Qi Lan (劉奇蘭)

Liu Qi Lan was from Shen County in Hebei Province, a very famous area for martial arts. Shen County is in south-central Hebei near the capital city of Shi Jia Zhuang. There are many frequently traveled roads that run through this county and thus large numbers of "martial arts bandits" inhabited the area and robbed travelers. In addition to the bandits, there were also martial artists who ran protection services. These martial artists were hired to escort travelers and protect them against the bandits. Needless to say, the martial artists in this area of Hebei were highly skilled. Liu Qi Lan's Xing Yi Quan teacher, Li Neng Ran, his Xing Yi brother, Guo Yun Shen, and four of Liu Qi Lan's famous students, Li Cun Yi, Zhang Zhao Dong (張兆東), Geng Ji Shan (耿繼善), and Wang Fu Yuan (王福元) were all from Shen County. Additionally, the famous second generation Ba Gua Zhang (八卦掌) instructor Cheng Ting Hua (程庭華) was also from Shen County and Sun Lu Tang (孫祿堂) studied his Xing Yi Quan with Guo Yun Shen in this area of Hebei. Guo Yun Shen's other famous student Wang Xiang Zhai (王鄉齋), the originator of *Yi Quan* (意拳) and *Da Cheng Quan* (大成拳) was also a native of Shen County.

Zhang Zhao Dong met Liu Qi Lan when he was still a teenager. Zhang and a group of his martial arts friends had all heard of the famous Xing Yi man Liu Qi Lan and wanted to meet him. The group got together and went to visit Liu to ask if they could study his art. In addition to Zhang Zhao Dong, Li Cun Yi, and Geng Ji Shan were also among the group. Most of these practitioners were in their twenties. Zhang was the youngest and thus he was known as "little brother." Liu agreed to teach them and thus they would all frequently travel from their respective home villages to study with Liu Qi Lan.

Li Qi Lan had many famous students, in addition to Wang Fu Yuan, Zhang Zhao Dong, Li Cun Yi, Geng Ji Shan, Zhou Ming Tai (周明泰), and Liu De Kuan (劉德寬), he also taught the well known Ba Gua men Cheng Dian Hua (程殿華) and Liu Feng Chun (劉鳳春). Additionally, Liu had three sons that studied Xing Yi, Liu Dian Chen (劉殿琛 - also known as Liu Wen Hua - 劉文華), Liu Rong Tang (劉榮堂) and Liu Jin Tang (劉錦堂). Liu Qi Lan's second son, Liu Dian Chen, was very good at Xing Yi Quan and Dragon Form Sword. He was similar to his father in character and studied with his father for many years. He was powerful and his technique was good. Liu Dian Chen wrote a book titled *Xing Yi Quan's Secret Skills*.

Zhang Xiang Zhai (張祥齋) - The Iron Lohan

One of Liu Dian Chen's top students, Zhang Xiang Zhai (also known as Zhang Chang Fa - 張長發), was very famous in Hebei for his fighting ability (see photograph on page 4). Zhang had begun his martial arts training studying Ba Gua Zhang in his teens with the famous Ba Gua instructor Cheng Ting Hua in Beijing. Zhang had moved to Beijing from his home in Zhu Shiu Ying, Hebei Province, when he was young and got a job apprenticing with a man who carved Chinese characters. He lived at his boss' home and would have to wake up very early, go to practice Ba Gua, and then return home before his boss knew he was gone.

After Zhang had been with Cheng for three years he returned home to attend a festival and ran into an old friend. The two friends discovered that they had both been studying martial arts, so they decided to have a contest. Since Zhang's friend was a wrestler, they decided to have a wrestling match. When the two friends fought, Zhang was beaten badly. Angry that his friend had won, Zhang said, "I will return in ten years and we will fight again!" Zhang then went to study Xing Yi Quan with Liu Qi Lan's son, Liu Dian Chen.

Zhang practiced Xing Yi very hard and after three years of practice he met his old friend once again. This time the two squared off to fight and Zhang immediately hit his opponent in the head with Xing Yi's "splitting fist" and knocked him out. When Zhang's friend came to he said, "You didn't use wrestling, that was Xing Yi!" Zhang replied, "It doesn't matter what I use as long as I win!" Angered, the wrestler stood up and came at Zhang. Zhang sidestepped the attack and then darted in, picked up the wrestler and slammed him on the ground. After this incident people began to call him the "Iron Lohan."

Later, Zhang worked as a bodyguard and martial arts instructor and made a reputation for himself as a ferocious fighter. On one occasion the famous warlord general Zhang Zuo Lin (張作霖) wanted to hire Zhang to teach martial arts to his troops. He invited Zhang to his home and asked him to demonstrate his *gong fu*. Zhang demonstrated a sword form, however, when he was done the observers did not appear very impressed. Zhang Zuo Lin's wife said, "I have heard that when practicing the sword, martial arts masters can have water thrown at them and will not get wet because the sword moves so fast. Can you demonstrate this?" Zhang replied, "This is not possible. You have read too many martial arts fairy tales." She appeared disappointed. Zhang said, "You have seen my skill, if you do not think I am good, send me away."

Zhang Zuo Lin bought Zhang a room at a nearby Inn for the night and asked him to return the next day. The general then called together some of his troops who were known to be good fighters. He planned to have Zhang fight these men in order to really test Zhang's martial arts ability. The next day Zhang returned. When the troops saw who it was they were supposed to fight, none wanted to fight him. The general then understood how good a reputation Zhang had among martial artists. Zhang Xiang Zhai died during the Cultural Revolution at the age of 96.

Wang Ji Wu's Xing Yi Quan teacher Wang Fu Yuan (王福元)

Wang Fu Yuan (1848-1913) was nicknamed "Iron Arm" Wang and was known as a great Xing Yi Quan master. Wang was senior to his classmates Li Cun Yi, Geng Ji Shan, Liu De Kuan, and Zhang Zhao Dong (also known as Zhang Zhan Kui) under Liu Qi Lan. Wang Fu Yuan was from Liu Qi Lan's home village in Shen County, Hebei Province, and studied with Liu Qi Lan for nearly 25 years. He studied Xing Yi with Liu Qi Lan from the time he was 13 until he was 37 and he never married.

When Wang Fu Yuan was thirteen years old (1861), he was sent to work as an attendant in Liu Qi Lan's home near in Shen County. Liu Qi Lan saw that the boy was intelligent and honest and after a period of time accepted him as a formal student. Wang Fu Yuan became the first "inner door" student of Liu Qi Lan.

After studying with Liu Qi Lan for many years, Wang Fu Yuan became an officer in the military and on one occasion was called upon to face a gang of bandits in Shen County. During the fight, Wang Fu Yuan killed the gang leader. From that time forward, the gang vowed to get revenge and threatened Wang's life. In order to avoid having to constantly look over his shoulder, Wang left town and went to live in Tai Gu, Shanxi Province. When he arrived in Shanxi Province he studied for a short time with his Xing Yi boxing "uncle" Che Yi Zhai. Che had been a classmate of Liu Qi Lan's under Li Neng Ran.

Wang Fu Yuan's power and skill were very great. He won the praise of many of the senior masters of the day. Once when guests had come to visit, Che Yi Zhai ordered Wang to demonstrate. Wang performed the set *Pan Gen** (盤根). He started off very slowly and gradually increased the pace until his queue was standing straight out behind him because of the speed of his movement. One of Che Yi Zhai's top students, Li Fu Zhen, was on the side watching and exclaimed his admiration.

During the time he lived in Tai Gu, Wang Fu Yuan continued to train daily. He heard that the Su family of Nan Mi in Yu Ci were looking to hire a martial artist as the head of household security. With Che Yi Zhai's recommendation, Wang got the job. The Su family was very wealthy, being the owners of several profitable pawn brokerages. While Wang Fu Yuan lived in Nan Mi, he stayed in

---

**Pan Gen* is a Xing Yi Quan exercise similar to Ba Gua's circle walking practice, however, the circle is very small. It is a three-step turning exercise where every step changes direction while the hands are held in a static position. The three step practice is trained so that the student can learn how to quickly evade an attack, open up the opponent, and then strike. The *Earth Dragon Canon*, which is presented in the section of this book on Xing Yi's Written Transmissions, pertains to the *Pan Gen* exercise.

the back of one of the pawn shops.

On one occasion, Wang went to Yu Ci city to see his relatives. The distance from Nan Mi to Yu Ci is about ten *li* (just over three miles). Wang set out at dusk and when he arrived at Yu Ci City the gate had already been closed. To gain entrance into the city Wang used his "lightness skill" and ascended the wall. After he had finished his business, he set out for home. Nearing his village, it was already near daybreak. Wang came upon a small river which was about ten meters across. He was always reluctant to display his skill in front of others, but since it was early morning and no one else was around, he decided to jump over the river. He backed away from the river and then first sprang forward about ten feet. When his foot touched the ground he stamped down with his right foot behind his left, and springing up from the waist, he sailed over the river to the other side. Unknown to Wang there was a man from his village who had arisen early and was squatting in the grass relieving himself. This man saw Wang use his lightness skill and told people in the village about it.

Besides practicing himself, Wang Fu Yuan began to accept students of his own while he was living in Nan Mi. Later he also taught students in Tai Yuan, that is where Wang Ji Wu met him. Over a period of thirty years of teaching in Shanxi, Wang Fu Yuan's students spread out all over the province. Many of Wang's students became famous in their own right. The famous "three Pengs," Peng Ying Xi (彭映璧), Peng Ting Juan (彭廷雋), and Peng Xi Tai (彭喜太), together with Mu Xiu Yi (穆修易) and Wang Ji Wu (王繼武) were the top representatives of Wang Fu Yuan. Wang Fu Yuan was instrumental in the spread of Xing Yi in Shanxi Province. Wang never left Shanxi Province and, unlike his Xing Yi brothers Li Cun Yi, Zhang Zhao Dong, Geng Ji Shan, and Zhou Ming Tai, Wang never became famous. Wang's first concern was in training successors of his art and in Shanxi Province his style has passed down to this day.

Mu Xiu Yi (穆修易)

Mu Xiu Yi was very famous in Shanxi province. The Chinese sold a brand of cigarettes called "*Wu Shu*" and put Mu Shu Yi's photo on the cover of the cigarette package because he was so well known. Originally he was a businessman and sold fabric, however, when he was accepted as Wang Fu Yuan's formal student, he gave up his business and only studied Xing Yi Quan.

In a mountainous area of Shanxi Province, called Mian Shan, there lived a Buddhist Monk in a temple whose name was Da You He. He was known to have "Iron Head" skill. He would ring a large bell by banging it with his head to demonstrate this skill. When he heard about Mu Shu Yi he wanted to challenge Mu in order to test his skill. At that time Mu was running a vinegar factory. The Buddhist went to the factory to find Mu, however, on this occasion Mu was not there. The monk told the others at the factory to tell Mu that he would be staying at an Inn outside the south gate. When Mu returned they told him about the monk that had visited. Mu sent one of the workers to go to where the monk was staying and invite him back.

When the monk arrived, Mu had a big dinner waiting for him. He said, "Welcome, please come in and eat." The monk said, "Thank you, but first I would like your instruction." Which is a polite way of saying, "Let's fight." Mu said, "As you wish. Would you like to fight with bare hands or weapons?" The monk said that he wished to fight with long staffs. Mu agreed and they went into the courtyard to fight.

The two fighters squared off and as soon as the staffs hit the monk tried to poke Mu in the stomach. Mu stepped back with his left foot and brought his staff around to whack the monk on the hand. The monk saw Mu's intended move and withdrew. Mu changed and hit the monk on the head with the very tip of his staff, removing a large chunk of skin from the monk's forehead. Even though the monk had a very hard head, he realized that if Mu's strike had of hit him on the top of the head it would have killed him. Mu had controlled his staff so well that it only removed some skin. The monk could feel Mu's power and recognized that his level of skill was superior. Mu's people wrapped up the monk's head and they went to eat. The monk said, "As long as Master Mu is alive I will never admit that I know *gong fu!*"

Wang Ji Wu's study of Xing Yi Quan

At the time Wang Ji Wu met Wang Fu Yuan he was Wang's youngest student. Wang Ji Wu studied intensely day and night for over ten years, training so hard that "his dripping sweat bore a hole through the rocks." Eventually Wang mastered the higher levels of the Xing Yi Quan art, received the inner teachings of his master and developed immense martial power.

After a period of time teaching in Taiyuan, Wang Fu Yuan returned to Yu Ci and Wang Ji Wu continued studying with his senior classmates. After a year or two, Wang Ji Wu returned to his hometown to visit relatives. While in Yu Ci, Wang visited his teacher and asked Wang Fu Yuan to check his form. Wang Fu Yuan told him that not only had he not grasped the concepts of the style, but

Wang Ji Wu (sitting) with a group of students on 2 November, 1974. Zhang Bao Yang is standing directly to Wang's right, Wang Jin Yu is directly to Wang's left and He Shou Qi is to the far right of the photo.

even his form was wrong. To remedy the situation, Wang Ji Wu quit his job and followed Wang Fu Yuan day and night practicing Xing Yi Quan. By the time he was 23 or 24, Wang Ji Wu was fast approaching mastery of the boxing art. Unfortunately, at this time Wang Fu Yuan was poisoned to death by a wrong prescription of medicine. Wang Ji Wu was heartbroken. He and his classmates took care of Wang Fu Yuan's funeral arrangements and took his remains back to his place of birth in Shen County, Hebei Province.

After Wang Fu Yuan died, Wang Ji Wu kept his master's teaching in mind and practiced harder than ever. He continued his study of Xing Yi Quan with the "Three Famous Peng's" of Shanxi. These three famous Xing Yi boxers where all named Peng, however, they were not from the same immediate family. Wang studied primarily with Peng Yong Xi, who was his older Xing Yi boxing "brother" under Wang Fu Yuan. Wang Fu Yuan had three famous students, Wang Ji Wu, Peng Ying Xi, and Mu Xiu Yi.

Wang Ji Wu's Bodyguard Service

After the fall of the Qing empire, during the early days of the Republic, the area of Shanxi where Wang lived was controlled by a warlord. Wang was opposed to his rule and consequently left the Province. Wang and two of his martial arts brothers, Peng Ying Xi and Zhou Bing Zhen (周秉贞), moved to Shi Jia Zhuang in Hebei Province and set up an escort and bodyguard service. They called the bodyguard service *Ren Yi* (仁義). The service quickly made a name for itself and Wang Ji Wu became known as the "*Ren Yi* gentleman." Together with his teacher's Xing Yi Quan classmate Li Cun Yi, who also ran the famous *Yi He* (義和) bodyguard service in Bao Ding, their Xing Yi Quan skills became very well known.

Wang Ji Wu with students and grandstudents on 20 September, 1975. Zhang Bao Yang is sitting second from right, Wang Jin Yu is to Wang Ji Wu's left, and He Shou Qi is to Wang Jin Yu's left.

**Wang Ji Wu with a group of students and grandstudents
in Beijing on 20 September 1982.**

Later, during the "warlord" period in China, Wang was "invited" to come and work for the local warlord army, but after careful consideration he declined. Since the "invitation" had overtones of "you work for us or we put you out of business," he had no choice but to leave the bodyguard business in Shi Jia Zhuang. From Shi Jia Zhuang Wang traveled to Tianjin where he went into commercial business.

The Martial Artist

In 1922 Wang Ji Wu was visiting Taiyuan and went to observe a platform boxing match. Liu Qi Lan's second son Liu Dian Chen (who was a classmate of Wang Fu Yuan under Liu Qi Lan), and many other of the elders in the martial arts community were in attendance. One of Wang Ji Wu's Xing Yi Quan "cousins" (his teacher's Xing Yi brother's student) was fighting a Chen Style Tai Ji Quan master named Zhu Yuo Jun (朱有钧). Zhu was undefeated, having beaten sixteen people in platform matches. During the fight, Wang started coaching his friend from the sidelines. The Chen master did not like Wang coaching his opponent and so he shouted, "If you know so much, why don't you come up here and try." Wang jumped up on the platform and immediately knocked Zhu on the ground. Zhu jumped up and tried to stab Wang in the eyes with his fingers. Wang reached out, blocked the jab and grabbed Zhu by the throat, lifting him off the ground. Zhu couldn't move and Wang continued holding him until he was about to pass out. The police came up to the platform yelling, "Let him go, you are trying to kill him." Wang released his grip and knocked Zhu to the ground. He turned to the police and said, "Everything is all right, we are just having a friendly match. No one will get hurt."

The next day Zhu came to Wang's room with gifts. The two discussed martial

Wang Ji Wu's students and grandstudents on 17 June 1984.

arts and became good friends. Two years later they met again in Shi Jia Zhuang. Zhu had become one of the chief martial arts instructors for the Guo Min Dang (國民黨 - Kuo Min Tang) army. Wang was carrying some luggage and Zhu told two soldiers to carry the bags for him. Wang Ji Wu's longtime student Zhang Bao Yang (張寶楊), who began studying with Wang in 1953, said that he met Zhu You Jun when Zhu came to visit his teacher in Beijing in 1954. He said that Zhu was the one who told him the story about Wang defeating him. Zhang said that his teacher didn't like to tell such stories.

In 1933 Wang Ji Wu settled in Beijing where he was active in public service, followed Daoist practices and studied Chan Buddhism (Zen). Through an introduction from Peng Ting Juan, Wang began studying Daoist methods of health cultivation under the Daoist master Huo Cheng Guang (霍成廣). During the 1930's, Wang joined the Hong Wan Zi Association and spent much of his time researching his martial arts, Daoist arts, and medicine. He was successful in reaching new levels of practice and it is during this period of time that he created the Xing Yi Quan Sixteen Health Exercises which are presented in this book.

The Patriot

Wang Ji Wu's students say that he was noble-minded, magnanimous, and above petty things. When he first arrived in Beijing he worked for a charitable organization and spent his time treating people who had been injured during the Japanese War. After the fall of Tianjin and Beijing, Wang put all his effort into helping those involved in the Japanese resistance get out of Beijing in order to avoid capture. One time, a local militia leader Zhang Qing Yu (張慶余), was beaten by the Japanese and he and his men were in grave danger. Although Wang Ji Wu did not know Zhang Qing Yu personally, he responded to the call for help and at great personal risk helped Zhang escape from danger. There are many examples of Wang Ji Wu's selfless service to his countrymen. One time some of the Chinese Underground Resistance fighters were captured in Tianjin and were being held for ransom by the Japanese. Wang Ji Wu organized the collection of the ransom and secured the prisoners' release. He was known widely for his sense of duty and generosity.

The Doctor

While in Beijing, Wang became quite well known as a doctor, especially skilled in the areas of bone setting and the treatment of external injuries. Many patients who had been plagued for years by various ailments were cured by Wang Ji Wu. His reputation spread and Wang continued his good work with characteristic enthusiasm.

In addition to fighting skills and *nei gong* (內功), Wang also studied Chinese medicine, bone setting, and traumatology. He later became one of the four most famous doctors in Beijing. Whenever he taught martial arts he always included the medical training and Daoist meditation. Wang Ji Wu's daughter, son, son-in-law, and sister-in-law all became skilled doctors under his tutelage.

In his later years, besides teaching his children and grandchildren, Wang Ji Wu taught many students Chinese medicine. His "inner door" disciples include, Wang Jin Liang, Zhang Bao Yang, He Yi Chi, Li Long Meng, Pan Ji Yuan and Wei Yuan Hui. Wang Ji Wu was recognized for his outstanding abilities as a doctor. Wang Feng Chun (one of the four top doctors in Beijing) and Chen Shu Ching (an expert in osteopathy) gave Wang Ji Wu the highest praise. Wang's medical training was a family inheritance. His grandfather, Wang Xing Kai, was a famous doctor of internal and external medicine as well as osteopathy. Wang's grandfather was unconcerned with profit and often treated his patients without fee. Because Wang Ji Wu was a martial artist, he specialized in bone setting.

Wang Ji Wu was always very fair in his treatment of patients, often foregoing the fee if the patient was unable to pay. One of the most valuable among the precious formulas for health which Wang offered was a set of Sixteen Health building exercises. These exercises had been passed down within the Xing Yi school for a hundred years and Wang put them together in a systematic fashion. After practicing these exercises since he was a young man, at the age of 100 Wang Ji Wu maintained a sharp mind, quick reactions, and perfect eyesight (he could read a newspaper without glasses). Wang often taught these exercises to his patients in order to speed the healing process. Wang Ji Wu died on September 13, 1991 in Beijing at the age of 100.

Wang Ji Wu's Xing Yi Quan

Wang Ji Wu's Xing Yi Quan training program is a very complete system for both health and self-defense. The system includes various kinds of *qi gong* and meditation practices, numerous solo forms, two-person forms, weapons sets, and power training. Additionally, Wang encouraged his top students to study and practice Chinese Medicine and Bone Setting.

When Wang Ji Wu taught Xing Yi Quan the first thing he would teach his students was a set of sixteen health building and body strengthening exercises he had developed based on various developmental Xing Yi exercises he had learned from his teacher. These exercises served as a conditioning set to help the beginning student's body and mind get ready for the practice of Xing Yi and then later served as a warm-up and cool down for Xing Yi forms and two-person practice.

This set of exercises was a vital part of Wang's Xing Yi training method for numerous reasons. Not only does the set condition the body by helping to open up the joints, stretch the muscles, and strengthen the tendons, but it also helps the student learn how to coordinate the mind, body and breath. The ability to totally coordinate the mind and body is one of the main goals of Xing Yi Quan practice. The "power" of Xing Yi technique relies on this ability. Wang Ji Wu's method of teaching these basic exercises to beginning students helped them to learn how to integrate the mind and body early in the training process. Continual practice of these exercises by intermediate and advanced students as a warm-up and cool-down facilitated the proper mental and physical preparation and conclusion for each practice session and thus his students were able to get more out of each practice. Additionally, regular practice of these exercises helped the students maintain optimum health and thus they were able to avoid injury and disease, enabling them to train harder everyday. The sixteen health exercises are presented in Chapters 4 and 5 of this book.

After students had begun to develop some mind/body connection, flexibility, coordination (internal and external) and balance during the execution of the sixteen exercises, Wang then taught his students the *San Ti Shi* (三體式) standing practice. The length of time each student practiced standing everyday or practiced standing before they started the five element forms depended on their constitution and their interest in developing high level skill. Those who had a strong body, patience, and were determined to reach a high skill level practiced standing for a long time. The body connection, whole body power, *qi* development, and mind/body harmony that are forged during long standing sessions are vital in the development of Xing Yi internal power. Those who were weak or who lost interest in standing would not be required to stand for too long. Wang taught two standing postures to his students. The first posture he called "single hand" *San Ti* and the second posture he called "double hand" *San Ti*. The standing practice as taught by Wang Ji Wu is presented in Chapter 3 of this book.

After learning the *San Ti Shi* standing method, Wang's students learned Xing Yi's five elements. Wang's five elements included *Pi Quan* (劈拳 - Splitting Fist), *Zuan Quan* (鑽拳 - Drilling Fist), *Beng Quan* (崩拳 - Smashing Fist), *Pao Quan* (炮拳 - Pounding Fist) and two variations of *Heng Quan* (橫拳 - Crossing Fist), *Shun Bu Heng Quan* (順步橫拳 - Smooth Step Crossing Fist) and *Ao Bu Heng Quan* (拗步橫拳 - Twisting Step Crossing Fist). Next students learned two different two-person forms, *Wu Hua Pao* (五華炮 - Five Flower Pounding) and *Wu Xing Sheng Ke Quan* (五行生克拳 - Five Element Creative and Destructive Fist). These forms are derived from the movements of the five elements.

In conjunction with study of the two-person five element sets, students also studied two different five element linking forms. One is called *He Yi* (合一 - Uniting into One) and the other called *Jin Tui Lian Huan Quan* (進退連環拳 - Continuously Linked Advancing and Retreating Fist). Next the students were taught another basic solo form called *Ji Xing Si Ba* (鷄形四把 - Chicken Form Four Grasping). This form was an important foundational form which later forms would build upon. After learning this form the students would then practice another two-person set called *Wu Shou* (五手 - Five Hands).

24

After building a solid foundation with the above mentioned forms, Wang's students would then learn Xing Yi's twelve animal forms (*Shi Er Xing Quan* - 十二形拳). Wang's twelve animal sets included the standard twelve animal forms (Dragon, Tiger, Monkey, Horse, Snake, Chicken, Water Lizard, Sparrow, Swallow, Tai Bird, Eagle, and Bear) plus the following additional animal sets: Jumping Dragon, Four Direction Monkey, Combined Eagle-Bear, and Bear Shoulders. After study of the twelve animal styles, students were taught another two-person form called *Wu Xing Pao Chui* (五行炮錘 - Five Element Cannon Fist). This form was followed by the combined solo forms *Chu Dong Ru Dong* (出洞入洞 - Leaving and Entering the Cave), *Shi Er Hong Chui* (十二洪錘 - Twelve Red Hammers), *Za Shi Chui* (雜式捶 - Mixed Form Beating), *Jin Gang Ba Shi* (金剛八式 - Buddha's Warrior Eight Forms), *Long Xing Ba Shi* (龍形八式 - Dragon Style Eight Forms), *Shi Er Lian Quan* (十二連拳 - Twelve Linked Fists), and other two-person forms as follows: *Zhou Tao Huan* (九套環 - Nine Linked Set), and *An Shen Pao* (安身炮 - Stable Body Pounding).

After studying the solo and two-person bare hand forms, students were then taught weapons sets. Wang's system included two Xing Yi saber forms (Continuous Linking Saber and Measured Path Saber), four Xing Yi sword forms (Continuously Linked Sword, Advancing Step Sword, Retreating Step Sword, and Four Gate Dragon Form Sword), three Xing Yi staff forms (two sets of Continuously Linked Staff and a Three Section Staff form), Xing Yi spear, Xing Yi needles, Xing Yi double-headed spear, and Xing Yi large spear. The large spear work was practice in order to develop power in the five elements (this set is shown in Chapter 6 of this book). Each of the five element forms is practiced with the large spear.

Wang Ji Wu's Xing Yi Quan Students
translated by Tim Cartmell

A Martial Artist and Martial Theorist: Wang Jin Yu
by Zhang Bao Yang and He Yu Qi

Wang Jin Yu

王金雨

Wang Jin Yu (1922 -) was born in Hebei Province. He graduated from Beijing University in the 1940's where he originally studied Economics. He has researched history and published several books. From 1980 to 1989 he was an assistant professor of ancient Chinese at the Chung Wen Television University.

Wang Jin Yu began studying Xing Yi Quan with Yuan Wei Bin (袁偉斌), a Xing Yi student of Zhou Ming Tai (who was Wang Fu Yuan's classmate under Liu Qi Lan) while in Junior High School. During the 1950's Wang Jin Yu became a student of Wang Ji Wu. Unfortunately, during the 1960's, Wang Jin Yu lost his left arm and he was no longer able to practice Xing Yi Quan. Wang Ji Wu encouraged Wang Jin Yu to contribute to the art by studying its theory. In the 1980's, Wang Jin Yu, with the help of his classmates Zhang Bao Yang, He Yu Qi and Pan Zhi Yuan put together the first draft of *Liu He Xin Yi Quan: The Written Transmissions*. At the same time, together with Zhang Bao Yang, he and his son, Wang Huan Sheng, published *Xin Yi Sixteen Exercises for Health* with a comparative analysis of both Chinese and Western medicine. He also wrote *A Treatise on San Ti Shi* and *Xin Yi Power Training*. Wang also studied *Qi Gong* with his classmate Hu Yao Zhen.

In addition to the above mentioned martial arts books, Wang Jin Yu has also written a number of other books including *An Examination of Ancient Literature*, *A History of Printing*, *Chinese Painting Master Li Ku Chan*, *Gan Tu Tong Ji*, and revised the *Home Encyclopedia of Child Rearing*.

Wang was a standing member of the first and second Xing Yi Quan Research Committees, is a member of the Beijing City Qi Gong Research Association, and is an instructor at the Beijing Ji Xian Martial Arts Academy. In 1991 he retired from the Beijing Xing Yi Quan Research Committee and now serves as an advisor. He continues his research of Xing Yi Quan.

A Famous Practitioner of Xin Yi Liu He Quan:
Zhang Bao Yang
by Wang Huan Sheng

Zhang Bao Yang (1922 -) was born in Hebei Province in the city of Xingji. After graduation from high school, Zhang moved to Beijing to begin working. During the 1950's, he began his study of Xing Yi Quan under Wang Ji Wu. He followed Wang day and night and learned the inner teachings of the art. Practicing martial arts morning and night, Zhang Bao Yang followed the advice of his teacher and studied with a humble attitude and open mind.

Zhang Bao Yang

張寶楊

Zhang also went to study with the famous Xin Cheng martial arts master Zhang Chuang Fa (also known as Zhang Xiang Zhai, see photo on page 4). Zhang Chuang Fa was a Xing Yi Quan student of Liu Qi Lan's son Liu Wen Hua (also known as Liu Dian Chen) and a Ba Gua Zhang student of Cheng Ting Hua. Zhang Bao Yang's boxing uncle was Du Ji San, who was a student of Bu Xue Kuan, a student of Che Yi Zhai. Zhang Bao Yang's teachers were all impressed with his spirit and eagerness to learn and were more than happy to teach him.

When the Beijing Xing Yi Quan Research Association was established in 1983, Zhang Bao Yang was appointed director. Zhang's enthusiasm and sacrifice in promoting the martial arts has won him the praise and admiration of his peers. His notoriety has attracted correspondence from martial artists all over the county. He was given an advisory position in the Ji Nan Xing Yi Quan Research Association, the Fukien San Min City Youth Martial Arts Team, the Beijing Sun Style Tai Ji Quan Association, and is a coach of the Beijing Ji Xian Martial Arts Academy. As Xing Yi Quan is an internal martial art, Zhang also studied *Qi Gong* with Hu Yao Zhen in order to deepen his knowledge of internal power.

Zhang Bao Yang is a man of many talents. Besides studying osteopathy with Wang Ji Wu, Zhang also studied acupuncture with Jia Chu Lian. In addition to his achievements in martial arts, *Qi Gong*, and medicine, Zhang takes pleasure in treating patients.

In order to further research Xing Yi Quan, Zhang and his classmate Wang Jin Yu have collaborated on organizing and editing the *Xing Yi Written Transmissions* and have coauthored the manuscript *The New Written Transmissions of Xin Yi Liu He*. In addition, Zhang and his junior classmate, Wang Huan Sheng, have written a book on Wang Ji Wu's Xin Yi Sixteen Exercises for Health.

In 1991, Zhang resigned as head of the Xing Yi Research Association, but continues his involvement in an advisory role. He is also a member of the Beijing City *Qi Gong* Research Association. In 1986 he began volunteering his time as a medical practitioner at a local hospital.

Zhang Bao Yang has taught many students. Because of his open teaching, his students improve rapidly and several of his students have become teachers in their own right. Some of his students have begun teaching his art overseas. One of his students, Du Fu Kun, has been teaching in Czechoslovakia.

A Practitioner of Xin Yi Liu He Quan: He Yu Qi
by Zhang Wu Ben

He Yu Qi (1930 -) was born in Hebei Province in Ding Xing County. After middle school he went to work in business and later in industry. He worked as an engineer and because of his skill was very creative in the field, eventually retiring from the Beijing Scientific Instruments firm.

He Yu Qi and my father, Zhang Bao Yang, were both formal students of Wang Ji Wu. He Yu Qi became a Xing Yi Quan student of Wang Ji Wu in 1952 and in the same year also began studying *Qi Gong* with Hu Yao Zhen. Because He Yu Qi and my father were neighbors, they often practiced together. At my father's request, I became a student of He Yu Qi.

Besides being proficient in osteopathy, He Yu Qi studied acupuncture under Jia Chu Lian. He is proficient in the martial arts, medicine, and *qi gong* and is a member of the Beijing Xing Yi Quan Research Association and the Beijing Qi Gong Research Association. Before retirement, he often treated friends and family members and now works together with my father.

He Yu Qi

何宇岐

A Practitioner of Xin Yi Liu He Quan: Wang Huan Sheng
by Zhang Wu Ben

Wang Hun Sheng (1954 -) is the son of Wang Jin Yu. He was born in Beijing and at seven years of age he was introduced by his father to Wang Ji Wu and became Master Wang's student, studying both martial arts and medicine. After graduation from middle school he worked for a time in industry. Because of his expertise in osteopathy (he learned the essence of Wang Ji Wu's skill), he began working in a hospital. Wang Huan Sheng was very popular with the patients and in order to further his medical knowledge, he entered the Beijing Medical College, graduating in 1984.

Wang Huan Sheng

王煥聲

Wang combined his knowledge of traditional Chinese medicine with that of modern medicine with excellent results. Besides his medical practice, he practices the martial arts everyday. He possesses considerable internal power.

In the 1980's, under the guidance of Zhang Bao Yang, He Shou Qi and his father, Wang Jin Yu, Wang Huan Sheng completed a manuscript of Wang Ji Wu's *Xin Yi Sixteen Health Exercises*. He combined his knowledge of traditional and modern medicine, martial arts, and *qi gong* resulting in a new perspective which was well received by the populace and contributed to their health. In 1986, Wang moved to Hong Kong and often travels back and forth to Beijing. Wang Huan Sheng has built a fine reputation.

In his own words, at the age of 100, Wang Ji Wu describes his principles of living a healthy life:

The heart is calm, quiet as still water

My own history is from the end of the Qing Dynasty, through the period of the Republic to the People's Republic, already a hundred years. My life has seen its share of ups and downs, times of poverty and hardship, honor and dishonor, the changes of the seasons, all of which have left a deep impression on me. After the founding of the People's Republic, my life became stable, but with the Cultural Revolution, disaster once again overran the country and I was forced out of business. All of these events served as a means of cultivating my spirit, and afforded me the opportunity to practice the "gong fu" of living in the world.

One must always maintain a calm heart even when influenced by the seven emotions; joy, anger, happiness, worry, sadness, fear, and surprise. The heart must remain as calm as still water, never allowing any personal desires to stir up a ripple of disturbance. My thoughts are pure, in spirit I seek to forget myself and transcend the common affairs of the world, keeping my life simple and my desires few. With a clear heart, I do not contend with others or make demands upon the world, but rather seek to contribute what I can for the benefit of all, aiding those in need and protecting those in danger.

Without desire one is strong, without desire one is quiet, without desire one may return to that which is natural, without desire one returns to the original state. With a heart like still water, from the extreme stillness will spring action, from the void comes that which is alive, *yin* and *yang* are in harmony and the *qi* flows unimpeded. With a heart like still water the *qi* is sufficient and the spirit full. When the *qi* is sufficient and the spirit full, the organs function normally, the blood is nourished, the meridians, nerves, digestion and circulation are all healthy and the metabolism stimulated. When the factors which prevent aging are all strong, one may prevent illness and live a long and healthy life.

Humans are wholistic beings which are possessed of a certain vitality. The spirit and flesh are inseparable and form a complicated entity. The human vitality supports, influences and is responsive to the person as a whole, while the spirit is the leader and controller, the "commander-in-chief" of the being as a whole. Under certain circumstances, it can be said that the spirit "pulls at one hair and the whole body follows" or at the slightest stirring of the spirit the whole being responds, and each movement of the spirit has a real effect on the individual. Therefore, I put special emphasis on the spirit as the leader, ever strengthening my resolve to cultivate the spirit, maintain calmness of the heart and become as pure as light without a speck of dust. This is akin to the meaning of a Song Dynasty poet who wrote "to understand the highest virtue," applied to the present time. Better yet, this cultivation of the spirit and heart will improve the physical constitution of the people, protect their health, and contribute to a long and healthy life.

Live an enthusiastic life, serve the public good.

I have traveled the long road of life, experiencing hardship, difficulty and I know the sentiment of man is often as thin as paper. I have seen corruption and those whose only concern is realizing their own desires. Because of this, I have strived even harder to live a practical life, willing to sacrifice even more for the good of the people. After the founding of the Republic, I spent my time working in the streets as a doctor, treating anyone who came to me for help with wholehearted enthusiasm. When one finds happiness in serving others, one will be full of the spirit of life, seeing things as they are with a calm heart. Thus, one may reach the state where the spirit is preserved within, the body is healthy and the spirit full, the intellect wise, decisions made adroitly and reactions made spontaneously. Consequently, the life energy will be strengthened and increased while promoting the health and longevity of the body.

Wang Ji Wu with his student He Yu Qi

Chapter 2

Liu He Xin Yi Quan
(Xing Yi Quan)
Written Transmissions

Wang Ji Wu with his student Zhang Bao Yang

Liu He Xin Yi Quan
(Xing Yi Quan)
Written Transmissions

compiled by Wang Jin Yu and Zhang Bao Yang
assisted by He Yu Qi and Pan Zhi Yuan
reviewed by Wang Ji Wu
translated by Tim Cartmell

Introduction
by Wang Jin Yu

The Xing Yi Quan, *Liu He Xin Yi Quan Written Transmissions* have never been published. These writings have been passed down and copied by practitioners and those interested in the martial arts, and used for reference purposes. Through its long period of being hand copied not only have several discrepancies in the characters developed but also some of the meanings of the original text have been altered. Therefore, it is impossible to avoid different interpretations and explanations of the text. It is not clear what the original outline of the transmissions were really like.

"A given culture is influenced by the state of politics and economics of the society of which it is a part." The Xing Yi Quan transmissions were written during China's feudal period. It is obvious that ancient feudal political rule was corrupt, this certainly had its influence. Today, under socialist rule, in order to "promote physical education and increase the health of the people," we should act in accordance with the saying, "in regards to ancient culture, we should not reject it out of hand, and should also not accept it blindly, but should judge and adopt what is useful." Also, "eliminate the dregs of feudalism and absorb that which is the essence of democracy." We must separate the corrupt practices of feudalism from those excellent things useful to the people's culture and democracy and the revolutionary cause.

1) In order to get as close as possible to the meanings of the original text, the commonly seen terms have been compared and chosen from several hand copied versions of the original text. At this point in time this version contains what is believed to be the most accurate rendition.

2) Martial arts are a form of physical education, the movements should conform to established rules of physiology. However, after a long period of being stripped away under a class structured rule, the art is rife with the dregs of feudalistic

society. Because in a class structured society, "all culture, literature and art all belong to a certain class, and all follow a certain political policy." Therefore, in regards to the "dregs of feudalism," we have already recognized the extent of their influence in order to delete them.

3) This volume is a result of continuous hand copied versions passed down. Therefore, the order of the contents and the length of the sections have been very difficult to keep in the original order without omissions. There are more than a few places where parts of the context are missing, or the content is confused and thus it is very difficult to say which was the correct order of presentation of the material. Because of this, in preparing this copy, we have temporarily omitted some of the sections, we have taken the information and included it in other sections, for example the sections on "body method" and "step method" are not placed in their original order. This does not necessarily mean that information included in one section is not also included in other sections, if information was relative to the section at hand, it may have also been included therein. When information is again presented in a different context, with different information, it should be viewed differently than before in relation to the new context in which it appears.

Although some information repeats, the reason is to give as complete an explanation as possible of the concept in question. Of course, although the body can be divided into sections for instructional purposes, it is in reality a singular entity. Bear in mind that although the text talks about the body in different and separate sections for clarity of instruction, the various sections are all related and must be considered together in actual practice. For example, there are separate sections for internal and external training, but in reality the two are not separate and unrelated. The text has a passage which reads: "If one wants to obtain the highest level of skill, one must strengthen the *dan tian*, if one wishes to strengthen the *dan tian*, one must first practice technique." This is a good example of the mutual relationship between internal and external training.

4) In organizing this text we have attempted to eliminate the superfluous and present the text without omitting its essence, it must be viewed as an imperfect attempt as our literary standards and level of martial experience are limited. We have perhaps chosen wrong characters, etc. There may be other mistakes and we invite all of our comrades who have a love and interest in the martial arts to offer their constructive criticism that we may improve together, in order to produce material that conforms to the science of exercise physiology.

5) Finally, this copy has undergone many revisions, and this outline is the result. I hope to make revisions of its inadequacies as soon as possible.

Wang Jin Yu
Beijing, China
New Year's Day 1982

Editor's Note: Wang Jin Yu and Zhang Bao Yang made a final revision to this text in September, 1993.

Dai Long Bang's Foreword

The vital points of Xin Yi Quan include: Yin Yang, Five Elements, stillness and motion, rising and falling, advancing and retreating, substantial and insubstantial, hard and soft. Its profundity relies on the six harmonies:

1) the hands harmonize with the feet,
2) the shoulders harmonize with the hips,
3) the elbows harmonize with the knees,
4) the heart harmonizes with the intent,
5) the intent harmonizes with the *qi*,
6) the *qi* harmonizes with the power.

手與足合
肩與胯合
肘與膝合
心與意合
意與氣合
氣與力合

If one improves day by day, gains complete knowledge, is brave in all circumstances, obtains an understanding of the principles, and unites with its essence, one will be able to come and go naturally, may be weak or strong, will be able to advance or retreat, can be soft or hard.

Dai Long Bang, 1750 A.D.

When the internal and external are united, this is the Six Directions.
When the Six Harmonies are mastered, this is the Six Ferocities.

Essential Knowledge For the Practice of Martial Arts

1) Solo and Partner Practice: For those practicing martial arts, eighty percent of the time is spent in solo practice, twenty percent of the time is spent with others. Therefore, it is said, "The time strengthening the body is long, the time defeating opponents is short."

2) Daily Practice: One must practice every day, barring illness, without break.

3) Humility: One must not show off or bully others.

4) Quality versus Quantity: In practice, quality is more important than quantity. To defeat a single opponent this is the correct method, to defeat many opponents, this is still the correct method. In comparison, the one who practices too great a variety will become panicked and distraught, if one does not train the body with a realistic foundation, in combat there will be no mature technique to fall back on, one will have neither a well trained body nor a solid technique.

5) **Perseverance:** There are those who talk about principles for a great length of time, they say martial arts are full of secrets. When you ask them they don't answer, or they answer incompletely. How can this be! There are those who are easily satisfied, or invite disaster by underestimating the art, or like to bully others. There are those who have no perseverance, who study a little and think they know it all, they are quite satisfied with themselves and rarely practice, they think they are a great success, until they have to use the art and find themselves useless. This is not the fault of the teacher but rather the student who has gone about learning in the wrong way. If these types teach students the students are lost and the art degenerates generation by generation. Where are the secrets!

6) **Important points for practice:**

a) Before practice: The stomach should be neither too full or too empty, the mind should not be preoccupied with other affairs, do not practice when angry. When hungry one has no energy, too full and the stomach will be injured. Extraneous thoughts harm the brain. Anger harms the spirit.

b) During practice: Do not fool around. Do not spit. Do not be disrespectful. If one is not serious in practice the spirit is dispersed, spitting inflames the throat, disrespect weakens the practice.

c) After practice: Do not eat or drink, do not relieve yourself, do not lay down. Food and drink will not digest well, elimination causes *qi* to scatter, laying down causes the *qi* to rise causing discomfort.

7) **The Three Harms:** Those who practice martial arts must avoid the three harms. If one is not familiar with the three harms, practice will injure the body. What is meant by the three harms? The three harms are:

1) Inappropriate use of strength,
2) Forcing the breath,
3) Sticking out the chest and pulling up the belly.

If one uses strength inappropriately, the *qi* will not flow smoothly through the limbs and frame, the meridians will be obstructed, the entire body will be restricted, the hands and feet will not be agile, the body will be bogged down by stagnant *qi*, wherever the *qi* stagnates illness will result. If one forces the breath, one will become stiff and easy to break, with the chest full of air the lungs will be squeezed and will suffer harm. If one sticks out the chest and sucks in the belly, the *qi* will move the wrong direction and will rise, it will not return to the *dan tian*.

8) **Seeking Instruction:** In order to study martial arts, one must be diligent in two areas. First, one must be willing to travel great distances in order to study with those of higher ability and sincerely request instruction. One must also be diligent in speech, humbling the self and asking for guidance.

9) Force and Self-satisfaction: In practicing the martial arts there are two things which must be avoided, the first is reliance upon force, the second is self-satisfaction.

10) Start Practice Slowly: Begin practice by moving softly, gently and slowly in order to soothe and open the connective tissue and bones, this guides the *qi* and power and leads it correctly. After a period of practice, it is good to use more force and speed in order to increase the internal power for practical application.

11) Sequence of Practice: At the beginning of practice stand in *San Ti Shi* (trinity standing posture), afterwards practice forms.

12) Stages of Training: After beginning formal practice, one must follow the rules of training, if so, in three years the basic training will be complete. In the intermediate stages of training, practice single forms repeatedly, use the form to express the intent. After a long period of practice one will be able to change spontaneously with the circumstances. After six years one will complete this level of training. In advanced stages of training, both the internal and external *gong fu* will be completed, your body will become as hard as steel, your *gong fu* will be of a high level. Therefore, the correct sequence of training follows these three steps:

Method	Principle	*Gong Fu*
1. Obvious Energy	Change Essence to *Qi*	Changes Bones
2. Hidden Energy	Change *Qi* to Spirit	Changes Tendons
3. Change Energy	Change Spirit to Void	Changes Marrow

San Ti Shi (三體式 - Trinity Posture)

The three "bodies" (*San Ti* or trinity) in martial arts refer to the head, hands, and feet. *San Ti* is further divided into three sections as follows:

Root	Mid-section	Terminus
Waist (*dan tian*)	Spine (heart)	Head (*Ni Wan* Point)
Hips	Knees	Feet
Shoulders	Elbows	Hands

The root, middle, and terminus is also known in Xing Yi Quan as the "three joints." All practice starts with *San Ti* standing. After walking through the forms, one must follow the correct sequence of training and must not omit steps. All subsequent movement is founded in *San Ti Shi*. This posture is the gate of the Way, it is the root and central nucleus of the art of Xing Yi Quan.

Wang Ji Wu Stands in *San Ti Shi*

39

The Five Element Fists
五行拳

1) *Pi Quan* (Splitting Fist) 劈拳

Rising Form - The two fists hug and move out from the center of the body in front of the mouth, the front hand resists upward at the level of the heart, the rear hand follows closely behind, the two elbows hug in close to the ribs at the height of the heart, the *qi* follows the body and sinks to the *dan tian*.

Lowering Form - The hands and feet come down together with the rear foot following, the four fingers are separated and the "tiger's mouth" is round, the front hand is at the level of the heart, the rear hand is beneath the ribs, the front hand, (front) foot and nose are on a straight line.

2) *Zuan Quan* (Drilling Fist) 鑽拳

Rising Form - The drilling fist resists upward at the height of the heart, the rear hand is hidden beneath the ribs, the two elbows hug the ribs, the foot rises, the eyes follow the hand, advance a step and lower the foot in continuous steps.

Lowering Form - When changing the fists, the elbows are hidden beneath, when the hands and feet lower together the *qi* will flow smoothly. The eye of the front fist faces upward, the rear fist is hidden under the heart, the front hand, foot and nose are on a straight line.

3) *Beng Quan* (Smashing Fist) 崩拳

Moving Away Form - When the fist moves out the three points must be on a line (hand, foot and nose), the eye of the fist points upward at the level of the heart, the rear hand is a *yang* fist and is hidden beneath the ribs, the front foot points straight ahead and the rear foot is toed-out (the character "eight" (八) step).

Turning the Body Form - Turn the body and raise the fist so it moves out from the height of the eyebrow, the body stands up straight and the foot is lifted, the hand and foot are lowered together into a scissor step, the front foot is turned out obliquely and the rear foot points straight ahead, the *qi* follows the body motion and enters the *dan tian*.

4) *Pao Quan* (Pounding Fist) 炮拳

Rising Form - The two elbows closely follow the foot as it rises, the fists are tight and raise the hands, the front hand is oblique and the rear hand is straight, the fists are at the height of the navel, the body faces straight.

Lowering Form - The hands and feet are lowered together with the three points on a line, the body is angled, the feet move straight ahead, the eye of the fist faces upward at the height of the heart, the front hand drills upward and presses against the eyebrow, the eye of it's fist faces downward, this is the proper form.

5) *Heng Quan* (Crossing Fist) 橫拳

Rising Form - The front hand is a *yang* fist and the rear hand is a *yin* fist. The rear hand moves out from under the ribs, when changing the hands and moving the hand out, the foot rises, lower the body and twist and the *qi* will flow smoothly.

Changing Form - The changing form of *Heng Quan* uses the "character ten" (十) step, the body moves obliquely then the step is correct, the rear fist turns over to become a *yang* fist and the three points are in a line, the nose and foot follow closely.

Pi Quan is like an axe and belongs to metal, *Beng Quan* is like an arrow and belongs to wood, *Zuan Quan* is like lightning and belongs to water, *Pao Quan* is like a cannon and belongs to fire, *Heng Quan* moves up and down like a spring and belongs to earth.

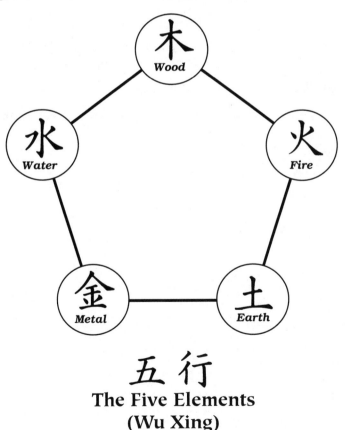

五行
**The Five Elements
(Wu Xing)**

The Mutual Creation and Destruction
of the Five Elements

Creation

Metal creates water so *Pi Quan* may change to *Zuan Quan*, water creates wood so *Zuan Quan* may change to *Beng Quan*, wood creates fire, so *Beng Quan* may change to *Pao Quan*, fire creates earth, so *Pao Quan* may change to *Heng Quan*.

Destruction

Metal overcomes wood so *Pi Quan* breaks *Beng Quan*, wood overcomes earth so *Beng Quan* breaks *Heng Quan*, earth overcomes water so *Heng Quan* breaks *Zuan Quan*, fire overcomes metal so *Pao Quan* breaks *Pi Quan*.

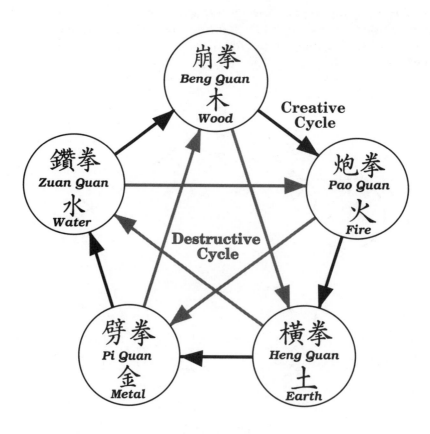

The Twelve Forms

Dragon, Tiger, Monkey, Horse, Alligator, Chicken, Eagle, Bear, Tai Bird, Snake, Chicken Hawk, Swallow

The Dragon is able to fold up its bones, the Tiger is brave enough to pounce upon its prey, the Monkey is able to roam freely over mountains, the Horse is able to kick with its hooves, the Alligator is able to move on the surface of water with agility, the Chicken is fearless as it pecks, the Eagle is expert at grasping, the Bear has great strength at raising up vertically, the Tai Bird is able to hold its tail straight up, the Snake is able to slither through the grass, the Chicken Hawk is able to weave through the forest, the Swallow has the agility to brush the surface of the water.

Twisting Root - The Earth Dragon Canon

The words of the *Earth Dragon Canon* are useful in attacking on the ground. Practice with the whole body, one will become strong and alert. That which is extended may become curved, that which is stationary may move. Curved, it is like a crouching tiger, it ascends like a soaring dragon. It moves and stops without leaving a trace, its extending and straightening are hidden. When the body comes erect it is like iron, its method is concealed like the dragon. Overturning violently like a tiger or panther, turning rapidly like an eagle. Going down is separated into front, back, left and right, the gates may change, there is no set method. When attacking to the front use the hands, it is the same for the second and third gates. When attacking to the rear use the feet, the knees follow in attack. If the distance is great then pursue, if the distance is small, go out and connect. When the hips are on the ground, lay on the side and curl the body. Falling backward is like sitting, it is like leaning back against a tail. High and low follow the intent, as do far and near and level or upright.

Editor's Note: The Earth Dragon Canon (*Di Long Jing* - 地龍經) applies to the exercise known in Xing Yi Quan as *Pan Gen* (盤根 - Twisting Root). *Pan Gen* is a Xing Yi Quan exercise similar to Ba Gua's circle walking practice, however, the circle is very small. It is a three step turning exercise where every step changes direction while the hands are held in a static position. The three step practice is trained so that the student can learn how to quickly evade an attack, open up the opponent, and then strike. The term "gates" used in the text above refers to the changing directions.

Three Fists, Three Clubs

"When the three fists and the three clubs are mastered, they become the three poisons."

Three Fists

Zuan Quan (鑽拳 - Drilling Fist), *Guo Quan* (裹拳 - Wrapping Fist), *Jian Quan* (踐拳 - Treading Fist). *Zuan Quan* is like lightning, *Guo Quan* is like a tiger treading, *Jian Quan* is like a galloping horse, performed continuously with one breath.

Three Clubs

Peng Club, *Pao* Club (炮棍 - Pounding Club), *Fan Bei* Club (反背棍 - Overturning Back Club). *Peng* Club is violent, *Pao* Club moves like the wind, *Fan Bei* Club is fast as an arrow, the truth is found within.

Fists and Clubs

The three fists and three clubs are not commonly found, the correct method is to keep a complete and tight defense, if one practices until one comes to the spirit of the thing, then one will become a first rate martial artist.

Xing Yi Sword

Advance Six Step Sword

Raising the hand, point to heaven and row the earth, brush the body and pierce the heart sword, split to the rear one stroke, from here reverse directions, lift the wrist sword, down to the earth tumbling body sword, landing dragon shape sword, swing left sword, advance one step split one stroke, turn the body and chop one stroke, central lifting sword, the black dragon tests the ocean sword, swing left sword, turn the body advance one step chop one stroke, obliquely brush left stance sword, scoop the wrist embrace the moon sword, turn right eight trigrams sword, brush the body pierce the heart sword, halt step intercept the wrist sword, lift the wrist sword, down to the earth tumbling brush sword.

Retreat Six Step Sword

Raising the hand, point to heaven and row the earth, brush the body and pierce the heart sword, split to the rear one stroke, lift the wrist sword, down to the earth tumbling brush sword, landing dragon shape sword, advance step chicken hawk overturns its body sword, step back and reverse directions, brushing sword, step back chop down sword, chop down destroy the form sword, turn the body and chop the head sword, the usurper lifts the tripod sword.

Important Points of Body, Form, and Martial Practice

There are a collection of terms or phrases which are often seen in martial arts transmissions, for example the "Eight Vital Points," or the "Fourteen Point Striking Method," and so on. These terms were used to summarize the knowledge gained through practice by those who came before. Because these terms were not created by a single man in a single time, some repetition occurs. Below we present a list of the commonly seen terms with examples. This should help those who are training in Xing Yi Quan, enabling them to utilize the experience of our predecessors. This will speed improvement.

Of course, for the creators of the terms and phrases used in the written transmissions of Xing Yi Quan they referred to first hand experience, for us the knowledge is second hand. Because of this, besides trying to understand the meaning of the written words, one must use even more effort in trying to understand the teachings in actual training, adding to one's own knowledge and experience. This is because true knowledge is only trained through practical experience. If one leaves practical experience, all that is left is empty talk.

Techniques come out like a pouncing dragon. Lift the hand like an eagle grasping, the form maintains the characteristics of chicken leg, dragon body, bear shoulders, tiger holding head. Quick as an old chicken, it moves through forms like a locust, its rising forms are like shouldering a yoke (it is also written, "move like a crawling bug, rise like lifting a yoke").

The Eight Vital Points

Wanting to obtain the ultimate technique, one must start with self training. The method of training contains both collecting together and moving. For those who practice martial arts, the Eight Vital Points are of first importance. The Eight Vital Points are the mother of Xing Yi Quan. Internally, practice the *qi*, externally practice the forms and movements. It does not matter if its the Five Elements, the Twelve Animals, the changes of substantial and insubstantial, rise, drill, fall, or overturn, all of these follow the Eight Vital Points. The Eight Vital Points are as follows:

1) the insides must be lifted,
2) the three hearts must unite,
3) the three intents must follow one another,
4) the Five Elements must flow smoothly,
5) the four terminus must move together,
6) the heart must be at ease,
7) the three points must be on a line,
8) the eyes must focus on a single point.

Editor's Note: The "insides must be lifted" refers to the lifting of the anus, pressing of the tongue on the roof of the mouth, and the lifting of the crown of the head. When the "insides are lifted" an "insubstantial energy rises to the top."

The "three hearts" are the *Bai Hui* (百會 - GV-20, "one hundred convergences") point at the crown of the head, the *Lao Gong* (勞宮 - PC-8, "palace of labor") points in the heart of the palms, and the *Yong Quan* (涌泉 - K-1, the "gushing spring") points in the heart of the soles of the feet. In "uniting the three hearts" the practitioner has an image of these three points being drawn in toward the center of the body.

The "three intents" are the *Qi* (氣 - vital force), *Li* (力 - strength), and the *Yi* (意 - intention).

The "Five Elements" are earth, metal, water, wood, and fire. Here the *Boxing Canon* is referring to five internal and five external elements in the body. The internal five elements are: the heart, liver, spleen, lungs, and kidneys. The external five elements are the tongue, eyes, mouth, nose, and ears.

The "four terminus" are as follows: The tongue is the terminus of the flesh, the teeth are the terminus of the bones, the fingers and toes are the terminus of the connective tissue, the pores of the whole body are the terminus of the blood vessels.

The "three points" are the nose, front hand, and front foot.

Twelve Important Points

1) the legs practice steps as stable as a mountain,
2) the knees erect and curve, and straighten like a pillar,
3) the crotch and hips inside and out scrape together,
4) the chest and back have a balance of hard and soft
5) the front side of the forehead knocks the enemy,
6) the three gates erect the shoulders and adhere to the back,
7) the two gates obliquely and vertically use the elbows,
8) pierce the bones and break the opponent,
9) stroke down on the bones to break the opponent downward,
10) brush inward to take the opponent's inside,
11) obstruct the outside to take the opponent's outside,
12) provoke and attack from above, below, inside and outside.

Seven Key Points

1) sink the waist,
2) relax the shoulders,
3) depress the chest,
4) press,
5) lift,
6) moving across or smoothly must be clearly understood,
7) rising, drilling, and overturning must be clearly separated.

To "sink the waist," the coccyx must be relaxed and slightly lifted, the *yang qi* will ascend toward heaven, this regulates the *Du* meridian (督脈). When "relaxing the shoulders," they feel as if they are being pulled back. To "depress the chest" is to open the chest so the breath flows smoothly and the *yin qi* descends. This regulates the *Ren* meridian (任脈). "Pressing" means the tongue presses the roof of the mouth and the hands press outward. "Lifting" means the anus is lifted inward. "Moving across" is to rise and "moving smoothly" is to lower. To rise is to drill, to lower is to overturn. Rising is drilling and lowering is overturning. Rising is oblique and lowering is smooth. Press upward with the head and then drill, retract the head and overturn, raise the hands then drill, lower the hands then overturn. Lift the foot then drill, lower the foot then overturn. Raise the waist then drill, lower the waist then overturn.

When raising obliquely the oblique is not seen, when lowering smoothly, the smooth is not seen. Rising is going out, lowering is striking. Rising is also striking, lowering is also striking. Rise and fall as rolling waves, this is how to rise and lower. No matter what, when rising, drilling, falling or overturning, the elbows never leave the ribs, the hands never leave the heart. This is the vital point of Xing Yi Quan. Those who understand have the essence of Xing Yi Quan. The students should consider this carefully.

Defining Terms

"Pressing the shoulders" is like practicing the steps, urge the rear as if erecting the waist, round the crotch to support the hips, lift the chest as if back-bending. The "shoulders" refers to the power of the "shoulder well point," sink down to the *Yong Quan* (K-1). "Urging the rear" refers to squeezing the buttocks together as much as possible. The crotch feels as if it is pressing across both inwardly and outwardly with maximum effort. "Lifting the chest" refers to lifting the chest as if resisting a force from the front. Relax the shoulders as if you are putting forth strength. Both sides of the back bone press forcefully together, the energy originates from beneath the navel, from the internal organs revolving outward to the head and then returns. When using the power of the shoulder well point, soften the intent and relax, there will be no obstruction.

Horizontal and vertical energies must be clearly differentiated. Horizontal energy is aided by the vertical, vertical energy is used horizontally. Vertical energy is from the shoulders to the bottoms of the feet. The horizontal energy is in the two arms. From the crotch to the bottoms of the feet, from the knees to the rear, they are described through legwork.

The power of the *dan tian* rises up the back and continues around to the chest, it flows to the stomach, it fills the organs, it solidifies the ribs, it rushes up to the top of the brain.

"Uniting" refers to uniting the entire body as one. "Erecting" refers to the vertical, horizontal, oblique, and reeling.

To stamp down is like stamping on a poisonous bug. When pouncing it is like a tiger pouncing on its prey. "Wrapping" is like wrapping something up so no part is exposed. "Comfortable" refers to allowing the power to be comfortable and open. To sever means to shake something until it breaks.

"To stamp" means that the foot has to stamp down with finality without further motion. When pouncing one must use the power of the whole body and the two arms. When wrapping the two arms leave no trace of anything still uncovered. "Comfortable" means the both the inside and outside use power. When the foot stomps it should sound like thunder. "To sever" means that when the two hands go out and enter they should use shaking power.

Xing Yi Quan Practice

When beginning practice, one should practice softly, slowly and gently. This will relax and open the connective tissue and bones, it will guide and direct the *qi* and power. Continuing with practice, one should use hard power and speed, this will develop internal power for practical application. The level of refinement is different for the above two methods of training. First one uses crude power, this is appropriate for beginning study. Later the power is refined, this is suitable for those with long time in training. This method uses fast motion practiced in intervals.

Xing Yi Quan has many single forms, these are to be practiced regularly. After a long period of practice one will break through without limit. When practicing Xing Yi Quan the time will pass, ten years will not develop the ultimate skill. On the surface it will appear that the later practice is not as fruitful as the earlier practice. Practicing a long time is not as productive as practicing a little. With maturity, the change will come, the internal power will be full, the external power will pull back in. Without many years of practice one will never reach this level.

Eight Character Secret

Chop (*Pi Quan*), Intercept (*Zuan Quan*), Wrap (*Heng Quan*), Stride (*Beng Quan*), Uplift (*Jian Quan*), Resist (*Pao Quan*), Wave (Alligator Form), Lead (Snake Form).

Sixteen Point Practice Method
(also known as Tramping/Drilling Method)

1) Inch: Inch refers to the step.
2) Tramp: Tramp means to go outward.
3) Drill: Drill is to advance.
4) Receive: Receive is to bind, the upper and lower bodies are bound as one.
5) Come: This is to scissor, the legs move with a scissor step.
6) Unite: This refers to the internal and external six harmonies.
7) Quick: This means to be (vicious) like poison.
8) Square: This means to be straight. If looked at from the front the posture appears slanted, if seen from the side it appears straight.
9) Passing: The rear hand rubs the fingers moving outward.
10) Lower leg: The place that initiates the motion of the four extremities. The gun hits its mark. Moving, the intent never breaks.

11) Rise and Fall: To rise is to go out. To lower is to strike. To rise is to strike, to lower is also to strike, rise and lower as the overturning of waves, this is rise and fall.

12) Advance and Retreat: Advance with low steps, retreat with high steps. If one does not understand advancing and retreating, practice is a waste of time.

13) *Yin Yang*: What is *Yin Yang*? Look at *yin*, it contains *yang*. Look at *yang*, it contains *yin*. In boxing, *yin* and *yang* mutually unite. They must be together.

14) Five Elements: The internal five elements must move, the external five elements must follow.

15) Movement and Stillness: Stillness is the original body, movement is the use. With stillness its use is not revealed, with movement there is left not trace. When movement and stillness are about to issue but have not yet issued, this is movement and stillness.

16) Substantial and insubstantial: The substantial is the essence, the insubstantial is the spirit. When there is both essence and spirit, then there is substantial and insubstantial.

The Four Terminus

The tongue is the terminus of the flesh, the teeth are the terminus of the bones, the fingers and toes are the terminus of the connective tissue, the pores of the whole body are the terminus of the blood vessels.

The Internal and External Five Elements

The internal five elements are: the heart, liver, spleen, lungs, and kidneys. The external five elements are the tongue, eyes, mouth, nose, and ears. The internal and external five elements are connected as follows: heart connects with the tongue, liver with the eyes, spleen with the mouth, lungs with the nose, and kidneys with the ears. In the boxing, the internal five elements must move, the external five elements must follow.

The Fourteen Points Striking Method

The head is the first fist, the shoulders (right and left) are fists, the hips (right and left) are fists, the elbows (right and left) are fists, the hands (right and left) are fists, the feet (right and left) are fists, the whole body is a fist, all together there are fourteen fists.

The Three Knowings

Clearly know the hands, clearly know the eyes, clearly know the teacher.

Body, Stepping, and Hand Methods

Body Method

In the study of martial arts the body method is the key and the way to profound skill. What is the body method? Vertical and horizontal, high and low, advancing and retreating, overturning and angling. Vertical refers to advancing from any direction. Horizontal refers to wrapping up power, opening and closing without obstruction. High means the body is lifted, it also means to increase one's reach. Low means to bend down, the form looks as if one is ready to catch and seize something. When appropriate to retreat, then retreat, guide the *qi* and return withdrawing and waiting for an opportunity. Turn the body and guard the rear, the rear is also the front. Pay attention to the left and right sides, then the sides will be safe. It is as if closed off and yet not closed off. Test the strengths and weaknesses of the opponent, move following your own plan, now vertically, now slow down the *qi*. Change according to the circumstance, one must not try one technique for all situations. Suddenly high then suddenly low, able to change at any time, one must not stubbornly insist on only one method.

Sometimes it is appropriate to retreat, then while retreating entice his advance. Advancing insures retreat. A successful retreat relies on the ability to re-advance. When turning the body to guard the rear, the rear should not feel as if it is behind. When guarding to the left and right, the side should not feel as if they are the sides. In all things, the eyes are the key point, they send information to the heart, the importance is grasped and the whole body reacts. If the body advances, even if the limbs are not guided they will move. If the body moves back, the entire frame will retreat as if on its own. The body method may be seen but not explained. The practitioners of martial arts should pay heed.

Close up the body and rise, lengthen the body and lower. Rise like the wind, lower like an arrow. Being struck, it is too late to blame being too slow. Rise like an arrow, lower like the wind, follow the wind and chase the moon without relaxing.

In regards to body method, one must not lean forward or backward, one must not tilt to the right or twist to the left. Move straight forward and lower straight forward.

When far, step close, advance knee to knee, stand up and use vertical power.

When the heart stirs the whole body moves, the five elements are all focused into one, be brave and succeed.

With the two words "rise" and "fall" the body is level. The word that "covers the world" (most important) is a centered body. The body is like a drawn bow, the fist is like an arrow.

Before the dragon arises there is first thunder, the wind blows the great tree and the branches sway.

The best method is to move first, the proper technique is the hands and feet arriving together.

The internal is lifted, the external follows, rising is horizontal, lowering is smooth, strike from afar, the *qi* urges the motion, the fist is like a cannon, like a dragon folding its body, when encountering an enemy it is like fire burning his body, rise and fall with the body level, enter straight into the center.

Able to advance at the appropriate time, one will not have to worry about survival, able to be ahead one breath, one will not fall behind.

When rising horizontally the horizontal is not seen, when lowering smoothly the smoothness is not seen, when low look high, when high look low. Rise and lower move with the heart, saving one at the point of death, dealing death at the point of victory.

The shoulders push the elbows, the elbows push the hands, the waist pushes the hips, the hips push the knees, the knees push the feet.

Step Method

When moving the body, the step is of first importance. The step is the root of the body, it is the central axis of motion. Since the whole body is used in an encounter with an enemy, the person who wishes to be unbeatable must rely on footwork. When advancing, retreating, turning or angling, the changes are in the handwork, but it is the footwork that allows the hands to adapt and change to the advantageous position. Advancing, retreating, turning or angling, without the steps how can one have a chance? Lowering, rising, extending or contracting, without footwork how can one execute profound changes? The saying is that the eyes are key and the heart decides the reaction, in all changes and turns of the body, in reaction to all types of affront, it must be that footwork is the leader. In addition, the steps must not be forced. Movement must spring from an empty heart, as if dancing without conscious effort, the body desires to move and the steps turn to all sides. The hands are about to move, the steps also urge them in motion. Without timing it so it is so, without making it go it goes, this is what is referred to as the upper wishes to move and the lower follows.

The steps are divided into forward and back, also fixed steps, also non-fixed steps are also footwork, like advancing forward, following backward, forward and backward proceed from a fixed step. If you take a forward step as if to the rear, and a rear step as if to the front, then a forward step could be an advance to the rear, forward and backward steps naturally do not follow any set pattern (there is no set direction so forward and rear are relative terms). For the practitioners of the martial arts, those who do not put body and foot work first in importance will not be successful in defeating enemies. This must not be taken lightly.

Come with a scissor step, the legs move in a scissor motion. Move the steps by inches. Come this way. Go this way. Advance with low steps, retreat with high steps, if one does not understand advancing and retreating they are wasting their time studying martial arts. It is important to have the correct sequence of movement, dodging, or leaping about the feet follow. Using the feet to strike the intent to stomp never misses, the feeling completely relies on the snapping of the rear foot. Keep feeling in the rear foot, and advance attacking with a stomping strike that shows no mercy. If the hands are raised without the feet rising it is also a waste of time, if the feet are raised but the hands are not raised it is again a waste of time. If separated by a space of ten feet, the steps must be fast, two heads turning, the most important is the inch step. The whole body is capable of striking. With footwork the entire body will be (as hard to strike) as air. Step straight in between the opponent's legs, drill in through his crotch. The legs have the ability to travel at a great speed.

The front leg relies on the back leg, the rear leg steps down next to the ankle, the rear leg relies on the front leg, the ankle is raised in sequence.

In regards to step methods there are inch steps, fast steps, and stomping steps, none must be omitted. In regards to legwork, there is lifting and drilling, lowering and overturning, not drilling nor overturning. The most important is the inch step.

The feet are seventy percent and the hands are thirty percent.

The leg steps into the opponent's center and steals his position. Even the most expert fighter will find it hard to defend.

Hand Method

The hands are able to push aside and turn.

If the hands are raised but the feet are not raised, it is a waste of time. If the feet are lifted but the hands are not, it is again a waste of time. Never move the hands for no reason. Dodging to the left and right, protecting both sides. Raise the hands like a steel file, lower the hands like a hook. The eyes must have a poisonous look, the hands must be wicked.

The elbows do not leave the ribs, the hands do not leave the heart. The hands enter and exit openings and the body follows close behind. Wait until the opponent's intent lags, then attack. The shoulders push the elbows, the elbows push the hands.

Raise the hands like a steel file, lower the hands like a hook. The eyes must have a poisonous look, the hands must be wicked.

52

Internal Training (*Nei Gong*)

The people of the world do not know what the internal power of Xing Yi Quan is. They try to guess from looking at the form, or suppose that we use much effort from the heart, or suppose it is some movement in the belly, these types of things have no effect, this is taking the false for the true.

In the martial way, it's form is the structure of its movements, its formlessness is its power. Therefore, the structure of the forms uses the power from within. If one has no power, then the form and structure is useless. Therefore, power (*qi li*) is the root of the structure. If you want sufficient power, the *qi* must be full, therefore, *qi* is the root of strength.

Those who practice martial arts must put the Eight Vital Points first. The Eight Vital Points are the mother of Xing Yi Quan. Internally, train the *qi*, externally practice the art of the movements. No matter if you're practicing the five elements or the twelve forms, or changing between substantial and insubstantial, or using rise, drill, fall, and overturn, one must never leave the Eight Vital Points.

If one wishes to practice to a refined level, one must strengthen the *dan tian*. If one wishes to strengthen the *dan tian*, first practice technique. Developing both the *dan tian* and technique together is the key to obtaining results. What is the *dan tian*? It is the root of the original *yang qi*, it is the place where *qi* and strength reside.

If the *dan tian* is lacking, the *qi* will not be sufficient. With insufficient *qi*, power will be inadequate. The five elements and the twelve forms will be empty. In this state, in defense one will be as a city surrounded by a dry moat, in attack, one will be like a strong soldier with a weak horse. One must practice diligently everyday. Sitting in meditation trying to become immortal will not cultivate the *dan tian*.

When using internal power, the power must follow the correct route. If one does not understand the proper routes of power and forces power out, there will be harm. The front of the body is the *Ren* meridian, the back of the body is the *Du* meridian, the *qi* follows flowing through. The *Ren* and *Du* originate at the *Cheng Jiang* (CV-24 - sauce receptacle) point, it moves straight down in front of the *Yin* point. The *Du* meridian starts at the coccyx point, it runs straight up the back, it passes through the *Yu Zhen* (BL-9 - jade pillow) point, the *Ni Wan* (GV-20 - mud ball palace) point, goes down past the *Yin Tang* point (the space between the eyebrows), and stops at the *Zhong* (central) point. The two *Jing* points issue energy cyclically. The shoulders have the shoulder well points, at the center of the shoulder. The *Chi* point refers to the *Qu Chi* (LI-11 - pool at the bend) point at the middle of the elbow. These are the places of the body which issue power. Through the myriad of changes, all are rooted in these, if the depth of this is grasped, one will sigh in amazement.

Qi ascends from the *Gui Wei* (GV-1 - turtle tail), cultivate the spirit in the *dan tian*. The coccyx is the extreme point. Use force to turn it upward, the true *qi* will naturally ascend. The *qi* descends to the ocean, first focus the heavenly heart. The center of the belly is the sea of *qi*. The center of the forehead is the heavenly heart. Its form shines outside. An inch or two below the navel is the *dan tian* point. One should diligently practice conserving the original spirit here.

One must be clear about the meridians, then look at the forms. The forms are patterns all beginners must study. If one does not understand them, there is no use talking about the meridians.

The head is centered then rises, the shoulders level then are free. If the chest sticks out there will be obstruction. Center the head and press up the crown, the countenance will be strong and the spirit full. The shoulders are alive and the back straight and level. With the chest out, the body wants to withdraw inward. This is the true crux. The feet are solid and stable, the crotch is solid and held in, the ribs are open and extended, when the feet move the knees use power, the front *yin* contracts, the ribs open, the true *qi* is regulated and even, the energy relaxes and tightens. When issuing *qi* the ears hear no sound. The energy must first be relaxed and then tighten, move it slowly.

First inhale then exhale, moving in and out. First lift, then lower, once ascending once descending. The *dan tian* is inside, it is the place the *qi* returns to. Inhale inward, exhale outward, never make a sound. While lifting inhale, keep the thought that the real *qi* is ascending to the crown of the head. When lowering, the real *qi* descends. While lowering, feel as if the *qi* of the whole body is infinitesimally small, it falls into the *dan tian*. A hibernating dragon or a sleeping tiger, latent and concealed. Contract the anus at the lower end, raise to the *Yu Lou* (jade tower), then past the pubic bone. Allow the *qi* to flow without obstruction. Do not stop it at any one point, the *qi* moves from the throat to the lungs and heart. Even though the *qi* gathers in the *dan tian*, keep the thought that it is in a low place. Rising, it has its route of ascension. The ribs are lifted together. Going down there is a route of descending. The *qi* rises along the ribs, open the sutures of the bone as much as possible, lift them upward, one will naturally obtain the key. Descending must start from the mouth, then it enters the front heart, this is the true route.

Breathe smoothly and evenly, once inhaling once exhaling, breathe through the nose. Then the *qi* will soon become stable. Proceed to inhale one breath. As you inhale imagine that the real *qi* is moving out from the *Yong Quan* (K-1 - gushing spring) point, ascends along the ribs, moves to the front of the chest, then it moves to the back of the ears, proceeding it ascends to the *Ni Wan* point. When the *qi* descends imagine that it moves from the *Ni Wan* point to the *Yin Tang* point, from the *Yin Tang* point to the nose, from the nose to the throat, from the throat following the spine and penetrates the front heart, from the front heart it sinks to the *dan tian*.

The eyes look at the nose, the nose is lined up with the navel. Moving from point to point one should keep still, pull open the twenty-six linked locks, a point of light will hang at the eyebrows.

Squeeze the anus tightly up and inward, the coccyx is raised folding up the bones, the feeling returns to the *dan tian*. Going forward it is also the *Que Qiao* route, at twelve it descends to the pool, lock up the monkey of the heart, control the horse of the intent, build the foundation in the bottom of the sea of the *dan tian*, one will feel joy without limit. Return to the source and pursue the self knowledge of the original heart, after a long period of practice one will have a body as hard as steel, the hundred illnesses will disappear and one will become as a child.

Combat

The key is the eyes, they send information to the heart. Their importance is grasped and the whole body reacts.

First stabilize the heart, the face smiles, the eyebrows look happy and the lips do not move. The heart is the General, the eyes are the vanguard, the legs are the war horses, the hands are the spears and swords, the heart, liver, spleen, lungs, and kidneys are the barracks and sentinels. The body is like a military encampment, the pores of the body are like a thousand soldiers and ten thousand horses. The body withdraws like an exploding cannon.

The sound of "Ha" is like issuing orders. Striking with the hand is like lighting a fuse, knocking men down without a smile.

The body is like a drawn bow, the fist is like a poison arrow, without a thought it cannot be stopped.

The best method is to move first, when the hands and feet arrive together, that is the true method. The internal is lifted, the external follows, rising horizontally, lowering is smooth, strike from a distance, the *qi* urges (the movement), the fist is like a cannon, like a dragon folding its body, when you meet an enemy it is like fire burning his body.

If you are able to advance on the moment, you will not be on the defensive, be a breath ahead and not a breath behind.

When martial artists fight, cover the five elements, the three risings are not seen, the three advances are not seen, it is all right if they are seen, it is also all right if they are not seen, move into the center, then it is hardest to change. When fighting with others, it is important to understand the "Three Firsts:" the eyes are first, the hands are first, and the feet are first.

When fighting with the brave do not think, he who thinks will find it hard to take inch steps.

Every part of the body may strike, when the feet kick, the whole body is empty. When far away from the opponent do not kick, the kick will not reach. When there is space do not strike, when there is space do not attack.

First strike the opponent's defenses then strike him. The whole body is able to defend. When striking, your own body should be able to adapt to circumstances at any time. When putting the hands out do not miss, dodging right and left, defend both sides.

When meeting an opponent, if you hope to be victorious, the four terminus must arrive together. If the hands raise and the feet do not it is a waste of time. If the feet rise and the hands do not, it is also a waste of time.

If you run into many opponents, swing three times and spin twice.

If the opponent's posture is good, do not attack. If the opponent is far away, do not attack. Know the near and know the far, know when power is early and when it is mature, know the wide and know the narrow. The upper and lower follow one another, if the heart stirs but the body does not move it is a waste of time, if the body moves but the heart does not it is also a waste of time.

Striking people is like taking a walk, look at people as if they are straw, attack like the wind, rise and fall as a drilling arrow. Wait for a moment of lapse then attack, when the opponent's attention lags, move on him.

Chapter 3

Xing Yi Quan
Standing Practice

形意站樁

Xing Yi Quan
Standing Practice

Introduction
by Tim Cartmell

Non-action is the real action. One hundred acts are not as good as one moment of silence. One hundred movements are not as good as one moment of standing still. Big movement is not as good as small movement. Small movement is not as good as no movement.

> \- Wang Xiang Zhai

Author's Note: Following is an explanation of the benefits of stance keeping and important points of practice. The information is my interpretation of stance keeping based on my background and experiences. My ideas, images, concepts and translations represent only one of many possible theories and interpretations.

Movement in Stillness 靜中求動

The internal martial arts have as a basic tenant the principles known as "stillness in movement and movement in stillness." This concept is related to the popular *yin/yang* concept of duality. The basis of all movement lies in stillness, which is the natural state before motion begins. If one cannot distinguish between absolute stillness and motion, there can never be true coordination. This is because part(s) of the body will always be moving either too little or too much, thereby decreasing the efficiency of motion. Beginning motion from true stillness allows one to control the motion to a very fine degree. One is strongest when the mind and body are unified and work in a coordinated fashion. This is only possible when there is calm. Obviously, it is much easier to practice and cultivate mind/body unity in stillness than it is during the performance of complicated movements. From this stillness is born efficient movement. The reason this is so is because with stillness and calmness come the most vital element to martial efficiency (and motion efficiency in general), and that is "true balance." Without true balance there can never be complete release of unnecessary tension and true relaxation.

A body even slightly out of balance demands continuous adjustment and an extra expenditure of energy just to keep from falling down. This causes undue tension and stress and effectively prevents optimal performance. Movement begun from this unbalanced state can never be completely efficient. Stillness in motion and motion in stillness mean when there is movement there is total, efficient, coordinated movement; when motion stops, it stops completely and returns to absolute stillness. Training of this type eventually allows the practitioner to mobilize 100 percent of his or her power and to focus it where it is needed. As with the acquisition of any other skill, one should naturally proceed from the easy to the difficult. Ideally, the training would be devoid of any superfluous movement and every action and minute spent would bring one closer to one's goals. The most efficient type of training which will enable the practitioner to develop a strong foundation, and many of the vital attributes necessary for martial efficiency, is standing still.

Stance Keeping 站椿

The foundation of the internal martial arts (and many external martial arts as well) is the practice of "stance keeping" or *zhan zhuang*. In the Xing Yi Quan system, stance keeping is the very core of training and develops many of the qualities essential to the development of martial ability. Over years of living, people acquire bad habits of body use and lose the original mind/body unity and suppleness and spontaneity that was their natural state. If one begins to train complicated patterns of movement before correcting bad habits, these inefficient habits of motion are carried over into the newly acquired movement skills and are further reinforced. Trying to function with inefficient posture or motion can be compared to driving a car with the emergency brake on. If you are driving your car with the emergency brake on, the way to increase performance is not to put a bigger engine in the car, it is to release the brake. Only when the car is running as efficiently as it should in the first place does it make sense to "soup up" the engine. Therefore, it is much more efficient to first inhibit and release bad habits and then, building on this foundation, train to increase power and ability. Stance keeping does both at once. It inhibits and eliminates poor habits of body use while increasing balance, strength and sensitivity.

The root of efficient movement is stillness. Therefore, a logical place to begin training is simply standing still. Standing still, one may reduce the number of variables to be dealt with to the bare minimum. The mind may naturally quiet and focus itself on the feeling of correct posture and true balance. The first goal of standing is to return to the state of "not-doing" anything, thereby inhibiting previously acquired bad habits and allowing the neuromuscular system to register the feeling of natural balance until it once again becomes the predominant state. Any movement initiated from this state of true balance will naturally have power.

Every teacher will tell you that the most important part of training is to build a good foundation, but many are not exactly clear what a good foundation is. The definition I offer is that a good foundation is mind/body unity with an absence of poor habits of body use which allows one to fully utilize inherent strengths.

Internal Power　內 勁

Although many teachers of internal arts like to talk about internal power and *qi* (氣) as something fantastic and mysterious (especially in the west), this is almost invariably a result of misunderstanding (on the part of the teacher) or outright deceit (because it is good for business). We, as physical beings, are subject to the laws of physics; mass, energy, and gravity. Our bodies are constructed a certain way, our minds produce real energy and we are all under the influence of gravity, all the time. The internal martial arts (actually, any of the higher level martial arts) seek to work with our natural strengths, to utilize our internal (mental) energies most efficiently and to produce the most effective movement relative to our environment (gravity and outside forces). The result is internal power. "Internal" refers to working with our inherent and inborn strengths under the guidance of the mind. Once again, mental direction is the key, one's actions and reactions are in harmony with natural laws and inborn strengths, rather than random, inappropriate external reactions to stimuli.

I have heard teachers of the internal arts talk about using *qi* instead of muscle force, and that no strength need be used as one's power comes from amassed *qi*. This sounds very profound and wonderful, but a moments reflection makes obvious the fact that without using muscle force and strength we would be unable to get up off the floor. The point is this, the externally observable result of movement is always a result of muscle movement in the body, the key to internal power is *how* the body is moved.

Many mistaken ideas about internal power came about because with mind/ body unity, correct relaxation and mental direction, a tremendous amount of power is released in an almost completely effortless manner. That is, the person issuing the internal power feels as if he or she is using hardly any strength at all. The results often appear almost magical. The key lies in allowing (not forcing) the body to use its inherent strengths in a coordinated manner. It is more a process of not-doing than of using effort, and such power must be directed by the mind.

In summary, internal power is only mysterious when misunderstood. It is the result of relaxing completely so the body's natural, intrinsic strengths can be fully brought into play (such things as mechanical advantage, the natural elasticity of the tissues, body mass, the stretch reflex, etc.) The whole process is under mental direction. The mind doesn't "control" as much as "inhibit" incorrect processes or tension so the body can function naturally. Finally, at higher levels of training, the vast reservoir of subconscious power may be brought under conscious control. It should be noted that the same mental and physical state that produces internal power is also conducive to good health, as one seeks to release stress and relax the body and mind while allowing the body to function optimally.

Whole Body Power 整勁

One of the special characteristics of the internal arts is their training and use of so-called "whole body power." This refers to coordinating the body in order to produce a maximum amount of power, much more power than could be generated with a section of the body (an arm or leg) alone. This type of power is manifest in all movement, although in different ways. Whole body power is based on relaxation and balance which allows the body to be used in a coordinated, natural way. The standing practice is essential for releasing bad habits and developing the essentials necessary for this type of power. Through standing practice we learn to relax and let our weight sink through the earth in a noncontentious alignment with gravity. We also learn how to become "still" and let the body's natural power work for us.

True relaxation and letting the body weight sink in alignment with gravity is essential to producing whole body power. Any superfluous tension or motion keeps the body tissue at the place of tension from contracting and expanding as it should naturally and without conscious effort (which amounts to a blockage which prevents one from using the power of the whole body). All the tissue of the body, as well as the frame of the body, have the ability to contract and expand, a natural elasticity and "springiness." When the whole body is relaxed and aligned with gravity (true balance) this springiness of the body is capable of producing tremendous power with very little effort. All that is required is to *let* the body move and react as it was meant to. Any forcing or tension only serves to reduce power. Here is a simple illustration. A falling raindrop isn't "doing" anything, but it still hits the ground with considerable force. The raindrop is only totally giving in to gravity and therefore it strikes the ground with as much force as it is capable of without effort or tension. No amount of extra motion of the water molecules within the raindrop itself will cause it to hit the ground any harder. To the raindrop itself, even as it falls under the pull of gravity, it is still (stillness in motion). Therefore, the two most important points in developing whole body power are relaxation and alignment with gravity.

The above is an example of using the body mass in accordance with the principles of relaxation and alignment with gravity. What seems to be relaxed and passive actually produces the most power as there is conformity to natural principles. Again, it is the non-doing and non-effort that produce the most efficient results.

In Xing Yi ,after basic standing practice we proceed to simple movements (five element fists) which develop the ability to issue whole body power in an efficient, easy manner which uses no brute force whatsoever. Finally, an added advantage is that this type of power begins from stillness, is issued completely and then returns to stillness (ready to be issued again immediately). There is no time lost in "winding up" or "cocking" a blow and no overcommitment which causes loss of balance or vulnerability. Whole body power can be applied to any type of strike, kick, lock, throw and even to ground fighting.

Standing Meditation 立禪

Finally, stance keeping is a form of standing meditation. The benefits to martial arts and health in general are numerous. We are seeking a mind/body unity, a kind of wholeness of being. Conflict in the mind precludes mind/body unity. As simple as it sounds, while standing one is taught to "just stand." There is no right or wrong, only an image of focus to which the body naturally conforms. The image itself serves as a focal point of mental activity which serves to calm the mind. There is only an attendant "feeling" and acknowledgment thereof. There is none of the nonsense about "not thinking anything" or "emptying the mind." The mind is focused. Trying to "stop thoughts" will only produce conflict and stress. While standing, one only observes oneself impartially with attention to how it feels, there is no conflict, the mind and body are unified and the brain waves settle down (not stop) into a calm state. It is in this state of calm and stillness that perception is clear, reaction is spontaneously efficient and one literally "rests" and "exercises" at the same time. This type of standing practice yields all the benefits of meditation while at the same time reinforcing mind/body unity and cultivating the body's natural power.

Basic Concepts
by Tim Cartmell

Relaxation 鬆

The Chinese word *song* is usually translated in English as "relax." This definition is incomplete and often leads to misunderstanding and consequently incorrect posture and movement. The concept of *song* requires further explanation. If you tense up the muscles in your arm as much as possible, you have created the state the Chinese call *ying* or "hard." If you let your arm hand limp and ignore it completely the Chinese say it is *ruan* (soft in the sense of slack). If you leave the muscles in your arm relaxed, but put your mind in your arm by using an image, such as your arm being pumped full of air, or that your arm is a hose with water rushing out of your fingertips (without actually tensing the muscles) so that your arm is now supple, springy, and alive, this is the state of *song*. It is a balanced state which is neither slack nor tense.

Song is a state of relaxation which includes the *Yi* or mind (intention). Although the body is relaxed, it is "charged" with the real power of the mind. This mind/body unity is one's original and strongest state. This concept of relaxation applies to the mind as well (although when applied to the mind the Chinese usually refer to the desired state as *jing* meaning quiet or a calm awareness). The mind is relaxed in the sense that there should be no conflict between what one is doing and what one thinks one "should" be doing. During practice, we seek to let go of any conflicts and pay attention to what we are feeling at the time. Remember, there is no right or wrong in practice, only an image or feeling that our body conforms to, as much as it is able, without stress or force.

It should be noted that just as true physical relaxation is the state free of excess tension yet not slack, true mental relaxation (*jing*) is the state free of any conflict yet not "dull" in the sense of daydreaming or "emptying" the mind until one becomes some kind of inert zombie. As mind and body are in reality one entity to begin with, the state of one has a profound influence on the state of the other. In fact, when one is *song* one is also *jing* and vice-versa. When one is lost, so is the other.

The other major benefit or true relaxation is that once it becomes the natural state there will be "stillness in movement and movement in stillness." This means that in stillness one is not slack and dull but rather contained within that stillness is an active energy (movement in stillness). While moving one maintains the feeling of calm and relaxation so only the proper amount of energy and power are used in the appropriate way (stillness in movement). Movement born of stillness and relaxation is most efficient and allows the use of internal power.

Finally, it could be said that *song* or true relaxation is the key concept in Xing Yi's basic standing practice. True relaxation allows true balance, it is the state free of bad habits of body use, making full use of all one's inherent strengths while in the state of mind/body unity.

Sinking 沈

This concept is actually inseparable from the concept of relaxation. "To sink" means to relax the body and allow the tissues of the body to return to their intended place. All matter naturally moves (sinks) to the lowest possible point under gravity's influence. The various tissues of our body are no exception. "Holding up" parts of our body only serves to waste energy, reduce mechanical efficiency and cut power. The only way we can fully utilize our natural, inborn strengths (the elasticity of the tissues, reflex reaction, mass, etc.) is if we are relaxed and "sunk" meaning aligned with gravity. Many of the images taught in practice have relaxation and sinking as their primary purpose.

We all enjoyed effortless poise and natural mind/body coordination as small children. Over the years we accumulate bad habits of body use and alignment; we began to separate our minds and bodies to the detriment of both. The first step in training is to inhibit and release these habits in order to effect a return to the mind/body unity, relaxation, poise and natural power we once possessed.

Much of the early training in Xing Yi Quan, especially the standing practice, is designed to reinstate true relaxation as the natural state. One stands comfortably relaxed while directing the mind with specific images which serve to inhibit and eliminate bad habits until one's original state of true relaxation and mind/body unity once again becomes the natural condition. With true relaxation and sinking, one will feel both "heavy" (rooted stably to the ground) and "light" (with agile ease of movement) at the same time. In this state, one is balanced and powerful while motion seems almost without effort.

Alignment and Structure 架構

The postures and movements of Xing Yi Quan are all designed to realign the body into positions of natural power. This involves lining up the frame so there is "space" in the joints and the soft tissue (muscles and fascia) are gently stretched. The result is an overall elasticity or "springiness" in the entire body which is the source of whole body power and unitary motion. When this type of body state is directed by the mind, one can make full use of one's "internal power." This internal, whole body power means to use the natural strengths of the body issuing energy in a "pulse" which is developed throughout, and supported by, the whole body. This type of power feels almost effortless as it is effected by "fulfilling the requirements" (setting up the conditions) for internal, whole body power and then letting the body issue the power "by itself." Once again, nothing can be forced but rather the alignments and movements are mentally directed. Forcing and tensing only serve to detract from the power generated.

The basic stance keeping practices of Xing Yi Quan are the primary tool for training correct body alignments in positions of power (positions useful in martial encounter). The human body is capable of withstanding and generating a tremendous amount of force. This ability goes far beyond what we normally think of as ordinary muscle strength (although it comes from the muscles, bones and connective tissue). The key to utilizing this natural "internal" power is to put the body into the correct alignment and then let the body function on its own. In fact, we use this type of power all the time in athletics as well as daily life. The goal of training is to develop and refine this ability and bring it under conscious control.

Use the Mind and Not Brute Strength 用意不用力

As stated above, we are looking for a state of relaxed awareness in which the whole body is supple, elastic, and alive. The only way to achieve this state is to use the mental to direct the physical. Not using force refers to what the Chinese call *Juo Li*, which can be translated as "brute force" (it literally means "clumsy power"). Brute force is strength inappropriate to the situation, generated by too tense or too slack muscles without mind/body unity. The way to avoid using brute force is to direct all movements with mental images which allow one to maintain the desired states of relaxation and mind/body unity and fully utilize the body's inherent strength until such movement becomes the natural state.

On the other hand, using the mind and not force does not mean we are limp and weak. Strength is used (if no strength were used we would be unable to move at all) and force is applied, but it is generated by a relaxed and balanced body, and the strength used is exactly appropriate to the situation at hand. The primary difference between the expert and the novice is that the expert applies strength and force appropriately while the novice applies strength inappropriately. The inappropriate application of force is the very definition of "clumsy." Use of "clumsy force" is addressed in the first of the "three harms" in the Xing Yi Quan written transmissions, "inappropriate use of strength."

It is important to remember that combat techniques are useless until they are a conditioned reflex and even reflexive techniques never reach their full potential for power and effectiveness until they are applied from a state of relaxation, mind/body unity and true balance.

Feeling Comfortable and Pleasant 舒畅

Releasing tension and stress and relaxation lead to an overall feeling of comfort. The postures, movements, and images of Xing Yi Quan produce a calm and pleasant state that is both conducive to health and increases martial power. Although standing is surprisingly taxing exercise (muscles will ache!), it is always practiced completely without mental coercion in the relaxed state. Many of the images will cause feelings of warmth, sudden release of tension in various parts of the body and a peaceful state of mind.

Exercise which puts undue stress on the body will ultimately begin to tear the body down. Sports and physical training which repeatedly overstress the same parts of the body make us succeptible to injury. All exercise is a form of stress which the body adapts to over time, this is the way the physical condition is improved and strengthened by exercise. But there is a world of difference between appropriate exercise which develops the whole person and mindless repetition of movements without mind/body unity which may prove more detrimental than beneficial.

Cultivation of Life Force 衞生

Although the postures and movements of Xing Yi Quan may vary from one style to another, they all conform to natural principles (including the laws of physics, body mechanics, mental and physical energy flow, etc.) and feel good. The mind and body are never forced and should never strain. Health is built up as the foundation of martial power. The Xing Yi Quan masters often said that the exercise must be *wei sheng*, or protective of life (in common speech *wei sheng* means "sanitary"). The broader meaning of this concept is that all physical and mental training should cultivate the life force and build health. The Xing Yi masters viewed extreme forms of training and conditioning which increased martial skill or power at the expense of one's general health, or which damaged the integrity of the body tissue as foolish and ultimately counterproductive. Training which involves forced breathing, conditioning the body by striking it with hard objects, and overtraining one part of the body to be used as a "weapon" often results in loss of health and function which eventually detract from, rather than add to martial efficacy.

In contrast, the methods of Xing Yi Quan emphasize that all training for martial power and ability must at the same time cultivate the life force and build health. The rationale is simple; people made weak from sickness or unbalanced training do not have the strength or energy to fight. This point is so obvious that it seems almost ridiculous to point it out, yet many people engage in training that, while building limited strength in one area, detracts from their overall health and ultimately robs them of their vitality and the ability to fight at all.

The postures and movements of Xing Yi Quan all promote health and strengthen the body as the basis of martial power. Another benefit to health is that stance keeping is a form of standing meditation. The mind is calmed and focused and unified with the body. This suppresses sympathetic nervous activity (which is active during excited, nervous "fight or flight" activity) and elicits the state the Chinese call *ru jing* (entering stillness) and is know in the West as the "relaxation response." The body is exercised as the mind rests. One may never have cause to use his or her martial skills "for real" in an entire lifetime, but each person must live with their state of health every single day. It only makes sense to practice a system which enhances both health and martial ability. The practice of Xing Yi Quan serves to increase both at the same time.

Although no type of training is a panacea for all ills or will turn us into supermen or superwomen, if the method of training we choose to devote a part of our lives to is not designed to cultivate our life force, build our health, and give us the vitality for all our pursuits, martial or otherwise, it is most probably a waste of our time.

Mind/Body Unity 身心合一

Our minds and bodies are originally one. Although they appear separate on the surface, they belong to the same continuum of energy which makes up the whole of our being. The almost unbelievable strength of babies is a product of this original unity of mind and body. All of the previously mentioned concepts (relaxation, sinking, correct body alignment, etc.) are tools we use to aid us in our return to this state. It could even be said that mind/body unity is the primary goal of basic training as it is the foundation upon which subsequent power and skill is built.

With mind/body unity the body is capable of functioning free of bad habits and will have full use of natural, inborn strength. With a return to this state comes true balance. One is balanced internally (mind and body in balance with the energy systems open) and externally (in relation to the environment, meaning gravity and pressures coming from outside the body). With this foundation, any type of physical skill is learned free of restrictive bad habits which detract from power and efficiency. Strength is built up where it is naturally required. In addition, any type of training undertaken in the state of mind/body unity is naturally *wei sheng* (protective of life), building the body and cultivating the life force as specific skills are learned.

Although the immediate goals of training are good health in general and martial arts skill in particular, the ultimate goal of training should be a complete and permanent return to the natural, unified mind/body state of being. Then one will be "practicing" 24 hours a day and life will be enhanced through a greater awareness of self and a more complete focus of the unified life force. And the starting point and foundation of such training in the art of Xing Yi Quan is stance keeping.

Postures and Images
by Tim Cartmell

Images

Our goals in practicing stance keeping are mind/body unity and a return to a natural balanced posture. In addition, we want to train the muscles and neuromuscular system in positions of power, that is, positions which will later be useful in martial encounters and which allow full use of our inborn strengths. Since we must never force anything but rather release and let the body return to its strongest state, holding awkward postures coerced by the will with force will only succeed in tearing down the body, reinforcing bad habits and causing stress.

The basic *San Ti* standing posture of Xing Yi Quan is erect and natural, with the arms held in gentle curves. Rather than holding a posture by force or having to constantly monitor for countless details, this standing method uses mentally directed images which automatically line up the body, release stress and bring about mind/body unity in a state of dynamic relaxation. For example, the instructor could give elaborate instructions detailing every angle, arc, and curve the body should assume while holding a posture, however, the stress of trying to remember so many details will be enough to negate all the benefits of practice.

One thing that makes Xing Yi's *San Ti* standing practice so valuable is that it has the most ingenious and complete set of mental images of any martial system. All of the images have been carefully designed and progressively categorized to immediately bring about the desired states of mind/body unity, true balance, stress release and condition the neuromuscular system to fully utilize one's inborn power in the most efficient manner. The images are simple and effective and the practitioner will be able to unite mind and body and coordinate movement from the start. (The traditional images used in Xing Yi Quan practice are outlined starting on page 73 in the section titled "Images from the Xing Yi Classics.")

Postures

In this section I will discuss some important points for all postures and movements

The Head:
The position of the head is the key to the alignment of the whole body. The head is at one end of our anatomy (the top) with the feet at the other. In order to relieve tension, elongate the body, and create the proper tone in the body tissue, we must gently lengthen or "stretch" the body from one end to the other. Correct tone in the body tissue means correct posture with an overall elasticity or "springiness" which creates proper space for our internal organs and systems while setting up the conditions for the use of internal power and the full utilization of our inherent strengths. If you want to stretch something, there must be an antagonistic pull at both ends. Gravity takes care of pulling our feet

downwards, what we must do is allow our head to be "pulled" upwards (meaning away from our feet, not necessarily straight up). So the position of our head is most important in determining the state of our whole body. When standing, the head is gently lifted upwards (with the mind, not force) allowing the entire body to release excess tension and align itself properly with gravity.

The Feet:

The body weight is evenly distributed between both feet. Let the weight settle on the entire surface of the soles of the feet (try to avoid putting the weight too far forward toward the balls of the feet or too far back toward the heels, also be careful not to roll the feet inward or outward). Make sure the feet are relaxed and take a moment to "feel" the ground. (This is the "double weighted" variation of the *San Ti* posture. If you stand with a 70/30 weight distribution, the distribution of weight on the feet is the same, the only difference being the center of gravity is shifted towards the rear.)

The Knees:

The knees are slightly bent and face the same direction as the toes. The knees must never collapse inward or bow outward. In general, we will stand up naturally, with a very slight bend at the knees. Later, if you choose to squat more deeply, remember the knees should never pass the vertical line which passes through the tips of the toes.

The Waist and Hips:

The hips are held level. Relax the torso and try to feel as if it is "full" on all sides (this means do not arch the back or collapse the chest). The *kua* (juncture at the front of the waist where the thigh joins the torso) is slightly inserted inward. Let the buttocks relax and sink as if you are "feeling downward" with your rear. The waist and hips form the center of the body and join the upper with the lower. This area is key to whole body power and efficient movement. When standing correctly, the whole pelvic area and waist should feel comfortable and free (almost as if it is "floating").

The Spine:

The spine is relaxed and allowed to elongate. This means there is no effort of the muscles to hold the spine or torso in any forced position. With the lifting of the head and sinking of the body, the spine will be elongated into its natural position and the stress between the vertebra is released. While some methods advocate "straightening" the spine by pulling the coccyx down and under, in order to reduce the curve in the lower back, this position is tense, tiring, and unnatural. The spine is not supposed to be perfectly straight, it has natural curves for a reason. We don't want to use force to pull the spine straight, rather, we release tension in the back and torso and allow the spine to elongate naturally. This allows the spine to have a natural "springiness" which renders it capable of generating tremendous power.

The Stomach:

The muscles of the stomach and waist are completely relaxed. With the lifting of the head and elongation of the spine the abdominal muscles will be gently stretched and held in the proper state of tonus. Although the stomach muscles are completely relaxed, because we are standing in dynamic, correct posture, the muscles will not sag or cause a "pot belly" effect as the posture serves to gently stretch the abdominal wall. Your stomach and waist muscles are exercised even as you stand still.

The Chest:

The chest is relaxed, widened and very slightly depressed inward. One should neither pull back the shoulders and stick out the chest nor slump the shoulders and let the chest collapse. The chest should feel open, wide, and relaxed in a natural position.

The Shoulders:

The shoulders are level and relaxed. They are neither pulled back nor hunched forward. One should feel as if the shoulders are poised and balanced at the top of the torso. It is very important not to lift the shoulders at any time during the practice.

The Arms and Hands:

The arms and hands are completely relaxed and always held in gentle curves. The elbows are neither bent too much nor rigidly straightened (the Chinese say the arms "appear straight but are not straight"). The palms are curved and made "deep." The backs of the hands are spread and the entire hand is open and full, allowing the mind and energy to flow from the fingers unimpeded. The fingers are gently spread and rounded, neither tense nor slack. The arms and hands should feel relaxed, somewhat heavy, full, sensitive and gentle. When holding the arms up, the weight should settle along the bottom (ulna side) of the arm with the elbows "hanging."

The Neck:

The neck is straight (but not tense) with a gentle lift at the back of the neck.

The Chin:

The chin is very slightly tucked down and in.

The Teeth:

The teeth are closed together without force (no slack jaws or grinding teeth).

The Eyes:

The eyes are level and look straight ahead. One may look slightly upward as if seeing far into the distance (as if viewing a vast landscape from the top of a tall mountain). Sometimes the eyes will be gently closed.

The Ears:

The ears "listen inside" to the "sounds" of the body.

The Face:

Relax the facial muscles, relax also the muscles around the sides of the head and the scalp. Make sure you are not wrinkling the forehead (frowning) by relaxing the space between the eyebrows. It helps to smile a little.

The Tongue:
   The tongue is relaxed and slightly curved, touching the roof of the mouth.

The Breath:
   Relax and breathe in and out through the nose. As you stand and relax, you may find you are breathing slower and more deeply. This is good. You can consciously relax your chest and abdomen to facilitate deep breathing but only "watch" yourself breathe, don't try to force or control the breath. When you correct the posture and relax, your body will naturally breathe in the most beneficial manner. Our bodies knew how to breathe best long before we were ever aware that we were breathing at all and will do so again if we let them.

   The above points generally apply to all postures and movements of Xing Yi Quan. They serve as a kind of objective view of the observable mechanics of posture and alignment. These points can be used as a "checklist" for alignment or as a comparative reference when analyzing one's own posture objectively (as in a film or photograph) or when checking the posture of another.

Possible Sensations

It would be very difficult, if not impossible, to pay attention to all of the previously mentioned details in practice (even while standing still). Besides, the fact that dividing the body up into so many parts would detract from the overall "feeling" of balance and mind/body unity we are trying to achieve. What is needed is a method that inhibits previously acquired bad habits while aligning the body and bringing about mind/body unity "all at once" without stress or tension. The images from the Xing Yi classics which appear in the next section provide such a method and tie the practice together into a unified whole.

Each of the postures and movements in Xing Yi Quan are designed to cultivate and train the mind/body unity and power for various types of *jings* or energies basic to martial technique. The types of energies trained in the *San Ti* posture of Xing Yi include many of the basic powers used in the application of the art and thus this posture forms a foundation for further study. Analysis of the energies cultivated in the *San Ti* posture reveals that there is an antagonistic energy, one of which can be considered offensive, while at the same time there is also a defensive energy, so the posture simultaneously trains power for attack and defense in the same plane.

Possible Sensations:

During practice, especially in the early stages, you may experience some of the following phenomena. These are perfectly natural reactions and feelings and there is no need to worry. Just relax and persist with practice and in time you will come to feel very comfortable as you stand. Despite the fact you aren't moving, stance keeping is real exercise. You may experience mild to forceful shaking in your limbs. This is due to a release of nervous tension or fatigue and will pass after a short period of practice. You may feel heat, cold, tingling, or numbness, especially in your hands. These sensations are also the result of the nervous system readjusting and balancing itself and will soon pass.

You may also experience soreness and aching in the muscles. The shoulders are particularly prone to ache. This is natural (just like soreness from any other form of exercise) and will pass as you become stronger. If your muscles begin to ache as you stand, try to relax and use the images to "take the pressure off." It may also be helpful to lower the arms and gently shake out the limbs and then return to the posture. If the aching is intense or you feel very fatigued, stop practice for the day and rest (these is no rush, power and skill are cultivated, they cannot be forced). Eventually, when you stand you will feel very comfortable and calm, as if you are floating in warm water.

Images from the Xing Yi Classics
by Tim Cartmell

The classical literature of Xing Yi boxing offers a wealth of images and practical instructions which are designed to aid the practitioner in aligning his or her body with the proper balance and focus of intent. The instructions range from alignments in relation to anatomical landmarks to colorful images. Below I have included the translations of some of the more relevent passages with brief explanations.

The Six Harmonies: (Liu He - 六合)

1) the hands harmonize with the feet,
2) the shoulders harmonize with the hips,
3) the elbows harmonize with the knees,
4) the heart harmonizes with the intent,
5) the intent harmonizes with the *qi*,
6) the *qi* harmonizes with the power.

The first three are referred to as the "Three External Coordinations" while the remaining three are referred to as the "Three Internal Coordinations." The movements of Xing Yi Quan are as natural as walking. We all maintain the Three External Coordinations during the motions of normal walking and this degree of naturalness should be maintained during the practice of martial forms. This type of natural motion is what our bodies are "designed" for, and consequently building a martial system around movements which make use of and work in harmony with our innate strengths will be inherently more powerful than forcing our bodies to perform "unnatural" movements (like fitting a square peg in a round hole.)

The Three Internal Coordinations are descriptions of the state in which there is no separation between desire, will and action. The trained individual is faster than the untrained individual because he or she has reflexive patterns of movement trained into the neuro-muscular system. The trained fighter has a desire to strike and the intent immediately mobilizes the pre-trained response, the nerves fire in the conditioned pattern and the body moves. The untrained person has the desire to strike and then must think about the details of the motion and make conscious decisions as the unfamiliar motion is made. In order to move as quickly and efficiently as possible the interval of time between the desire to move (heart), the actual specific mental directions to move (intent), the neuro-muscular reactions to the impulse of the intent (*qi*) and the actual motion itself (power) must be as short as possible.

The Eight Words (Ba Zi - 八字):

The eight words provide the practitioner with images used in aligning the body and using strength naturally. Each of the eight words has three important points. The eight words are as follows: Press, Close, Round, Sensitive, Hold, Sink, Curve, and Extend. Each word has three places of application on the body as follows:

The Three Pressings (San Ding - 三頂): The head presses upward, the palms press outward and the tongue presses against the roof of the mouth.

The Three Closings (San Kou - 三扣): The shoulders feel as if they will close together, the back of the hands and feet feel as if they are closing together and the teeth close together.

The Three Roundings (San Yuan - 三圓): The back is round, the chest is round, and the Tiger's Mouth (space between the thumb and index finger) is round.

The Three Sensitivities (San Min - 三敏): The heart is sensitive, the eyes are sensitive, and the hands are sensitive.

The Three Holdings (San Bao - 三抱): Hold the *dan tian*, hold the *qi* of the heart, hold the ribs.

The Three Sinkings (San Chui - 三垂): The *qi* sinks, the shoulders sink and the elbows sink.

The Three Curves (San Qu - 三曲): The arms are curved, the knees are curved, and the wrists are curved.

The Three Extensions (San Ting - 三挺): The neck is extended (lengthened), the spine is extened and the knees are extended.

(Note: For details please refer to the important points for postures at the beginning of this section.)

The Five Bows (Wu Gong - 五弓):

The two arms, two legs, and spine are imagined to be bows. The arms and legs are slightly curved (like a drawn bow) with the intent of extending (as if to release an arrow). A kinesthetic sense of this image fills the body with a kind of "elastic" power which is neither rigid nor slack. The spine is extended and the head presses upward but there is a slight feeling of a drawn curve because the shoulders and arms are extended forward.

The Four Levels (Si Ping - 四平):

The top of the head, the two eyes, the shoulders, and the hips are all held "level," meaning parallel to the ground. These alignments are relatively simple to understand and feel, and along with the pressing up of the head go a long way towards aligning the whole body.

Sticking out the chest, pulling in the stomach, forcing the breath, and using brute force will harm the body.

These are some of the most common mistakes of beginners. To avoid these mistakes the chest is held normally without pushing it out or letting it collapse inward. The stomach must be relaxed so that the breathing is not restricted and the waist is relaxed and able to move freely. Forcing the breath refers to holding the air in during physical exertion. Finally, brute force refers to the extra tension caused by a body out of alignment or using one part of the body without the support of the whole.

Three Points on a Line (San Jian Yao Zhao - 三尖要照):

The tip of the nose, the tip of the front hand and the tip of the front foot are all on the same verticle plane. This passage is related to the Three External Coordinations of the Six Harmonies. When this alignment is correct, one automatically has the Three External Coordinations.

The Fists do not Leave the Heart, the Arms (Elbows) do not Leave the Ribs:

Once again, this passage is related to the Three External Coordinations. The hands do not move very far from the centerline of the body before the body begins to turn. The elbows do not lift up away from the ribs (sink the elbows) nor are the arms extended too far to the front.

Finally, the position and shape of the various parts of the body are compared to animals. These images are related to the eight words and say the same thing in a strongly imaginitive way. The animal/body connections are as follows:

Chicken Leg (Ji Tui - 鷄腿)
Dragon Body (Long Shen - 龍身)
Eagle Claw (Ying Zhao - 鷹爪)
Bear Shoulers (Xiong Bang - 熊膀)
Tiger's Head Embrace (Hu Bao Tou - 虎抱頭)

Practicing San Ti Shi
Wang Ji Wu's Method
by Dan Miller and Tim Cartmell

三體式

The *Boxing Canon* states:
   "The three bodies (*San Ti*) in martial arts refer to the head, hands, and feet. *San Ti* is further divided into three sections as follows:

Root	Mid-section	Terminus
Waist (*dan tian*)	Spine (heart)	Head (*Ni Wan* Point)
Hips	Knees	Feet
Shoulders	Elbows	Hands

   All Xing Yi Quan practice starts with *San Ti* standing. After walking through the forms, one must follow the correct sequence of training and must not omit steps. All subsequent movement is founded in *San Ti Shi*. This posture is the gate of the Way, it is the root and central nucleus of the art of Xing Yi Quan."

   Almost every system of Xing Yi Quan in Northern China has the practice of standing silently in *San Ti Shi* at its foundation. While one will find slight variations in the exact body positions and alignments from one style to the next, all standing practice adheres to certain principles. In September of 1993 and April of 1994, we discussed Wang Ji Wu's *San Ti* standing practice with two of his top students, Zhang Bao Yang and Wang Jin Yu. In this section we will discuss the general principles as well as the specific details of the standing practice in this system of Xing Yi Quan.
   Wang Ji Wu taught his students two versions of the *San Ti* posture, one he called "single hand" *San Ti* and the other "double hand" *San Ti* (see photos the next page). In the Shanxi style of Xing Yi Quan, the "single hand" *San Ti* posture is typically assumed as a beginning transition into the form movements and the "double hand" *San Ti* posture is assumed when ending the forms. In our discussions, Zhang Bao Yang and Wang Jin Yu said that in practicing the *San Ti* standing posture, the student "trains to keep his or her center." By knowing how to always "keep his center" the student will always be stable and have good balance while being very agile at the same time. In addition to developing an awareness of one's center, strengthening the legs, and developing a strong root, the alignments of this posture also develop internal energy and integrate the whole body.

"Single Hand" *San Ti Shi*   **"Double Hand"** *San Ti Shi*

Zhang and Wang said that the most important fundamental principles to remember when practicing *San Ti* standing are outlined in the *Boxing Canon* in the "Six Harmonies" and "Eight Vital Points." These principles are as follows:

Eight Vital Points:

1) the insides must be lifted,
2) the three hearts must unite,
3) the three intents must follow one another,
4) the Five Elements must flow smoothly,
5) the four terminus must move together,
6) the heart must be at ease,
7) the three points must be on a line,
8) the eyes must focus on a single point.

Six Harmonies: 六合

1) the hands harmonize with the feet,
2) the shoulders harmonize with the hips,
3) the elbows harmonize with the knees,
4) the heart harmonizes with the intent,
5) the intent harmonizes with the *qi*,
6) the *qi* harmonizes with the power.

Wang Ji Wu's *San Ti* Standing Postures

Posture One: "Single Hand" *San Ti Shi*

Beginning Posture: The *San Ti* standing practice begins with the practitioner standing in a relaxed natural posture as shown in photograph #1 on the next page. Stand up naturally, the heels together, the toes pointing outward at a 60 degree angle (60 degree angle between them). The whole body is relaxed and comfortable, do not stand stiffly. The eyes look straight ahead, close the mouth, the tongue touches the roof of the mouth, breathe naturally, imagine the breath moves in and out of the *dan tian*, concentrate the spirit and quiet the *qi*. The two arms are relaxed, hands at the sides. The heart is as quiet as still water. The crown of the head gently presses upward. Now you are prepared for movement.

Transition Posture: From the beginning stance the weight shifts to the right leg, the knees bend slightly, and the left leg raises up off the ground slightly into a "chicken" stance. The hands move up to a position in front of the heart with the right hand resting on top of the left hand, the fingers of both hands pointing straight ahead (see photograph #2). The body remains relaxed. Ensure that the shoulders remain relaxed and the elbows are dropped down when the hands are brought up.

The "Single Hand" San Ti Posture: From the transitional posture of photograph #2, the right leg stays in place while the left leg steps out and the weight settles at 50/50. At the same time, the left hand pushes forward and extends out in front of the heart while the right hand pulls back, the root of the thumb rests against the navel (see photograph #3). The hips turn 45 degrees with the front hip being forward. A detailed description of this posture is given below.

The Head:
    The head is gently lifted upwards and tilted slightly forward. The forward tilt is facilitated by the eyes looking at the *hu kou* (LI-4) or "tiger's mouth" (a point near where the thumb and index finger meet) of the forward hand. While the head in general is gently lifted upward, the *bai hui* point at the crown of the head has a feeling of being gently sucked inward. While many standing methods call for one to lift up at this point, Wang Ji Wu's method calls for the head to be gently lifted up, the neck gently stretched in back while the chin is gently tucked in and the *bai hui* point to have a feeling of being sucked inward.

The Feet:
    The weight of the body is evenly distributed in both legs (50/50 weighted). While many methods of *San Ti* standing call for the weight distribution to be 70/30 or 60/40 (especially in the Hebei styles of Xing Yi), the 50/50 weight distribution is typical of the Xing Yi in Shanxi Province. Zhang Bao Yang explains that they emphasize the 50/50 weighted stance in their system because one can be more agile in both directions (forward and backward). He states that the 70/30 or 60/40 stance is more "active forward" while in the 50/50 stance the

Photo #1

Photo #2

Photo #3

practitioner is ready to move in either direction. Their method of Xing Yi utilizes quick, short, strong steps which are best launched from the 50/50 stance. He also says that standing with this weight distribution develops a strong central equilibrium and a deep root. It is easier to develop an awareness of your center from this posture.

The toes have a feeling of grasping the ground. The heels feel as if they want to move outward (away from your center) and the toes feel as if they want to move inward (towards your center). The *yong quan* (K-1) or "bubbling well" points in the hearts of both feet have the feeling of being pulled upward. The forward foot points forward while the rear foot angles outward at 45 degrees. The back leg has a feeling of being ready to move as if wanting to spring the body forward.

The Knees:

The knees are slightly bent and face the same direction as the toes. The knees must never collapse inward or bow outward. In general, stand up naturally, with a very slight bend at the knees. The forward knee is positioned such that the forward shin is approximately perpendicular to the ground.

The Waist and Hips:

The body is divided into three sections; from the top of the head to the hips is one section, from the hips to the knees is the second section and from the knees to the feet is the third section. The waist is the area that joins the upper and lower body. The waist must be relaxed with the *qi* and breath sunk into the *dan tian* so that a movement from the center moves the whole body in a coordinated fashion. This is a key to whole body power.

The Chest:

The chest must never be stuck out and is held slightly depressed. As the shoulders are pulled forward the chest will have the appearance of "emptying" into the *dan tian*. This facilitates the alignment of the shoulders and hips.

The Shoulders:

The shoulders are level and relaxed. They are never pulled back nor hunched forward. One should feel as if the shoulders are poised and balanced at the top of the torso. It is very important not to lift the shoulders at any time during the practice. In accordance with the "six harmonies" the shoulders are aligned with the hips. However, as one will notice from the photos of Zhang Bao Yang on the next page, this alignment is not exactly vertical. Because of the 50/50 weighted stance, the weight of the body falls in-between the legs. The shoulders are kept forward of the hips, and the spine is straight. This alignment facilitates a direct line from the back heel to the hips, along the spine, to the shoulders and then up through the top of the head. Photograph #4 on the next page clearly illustrates this alignment. If you were to draw a line from Zhang Bao Yang's head to his back heel, you would notice that the spine will be parallel to this line and the alignment of the hips and shoulders are also parallel to this line. This alignment is characteristic of Shanxi style Xing Yi.

Photo #4

Photo #5

The Arms and Hands:

In accordance with the requirements of the "three curves," the arms and hands are and always held in gentle curves. They are relaxed, however, there is intention all the way out to the finger tips. This means that the hands are relaxed, but they are not slack. The elbows are neither bent too much nor rigidly straightened (the Chinese say the arms "appear straight but are not straight, appear bent but are not bent"). The wrists are relaxed and held in a line with the forearms, curved slightly outward and upward. The palms are curved and made "deep" or "hollow" at the *lao gong* (PC-8) point in the center of the palm.

The backs of the hands are spread and the fingers are spread apart like an eagle's talon. The fingers are gently spread and rounded, neither tense nor slack. The three outside fingers of each hand are curved slightly as if one is preparing to grasp something. This builds "digging power." The "tiger's mouth" is rounded as the thumb is stretched away from the index finger. Beginning students should only curve the fingers slightly, more advanced students can curve the fingers to a greater degree (as shown in photograph #3 on page 79). If a beginner bends the fingers as much as Wang Ji Wu has his bent in the photograph, the fingers will tend to be limp as the beginning student has not yet developed the proper intention or power in the hands. The beginner should bend the fingers as Zhang Bao Yang demonstrates in the two photos above.

The elbows must always hang and feel as if they are "sinking." The weight of the shoulders presses the elbows. In turn, the heaviness of the elbows is mentally transferred to the hands.

The forward palm maintains the feeling of pushing forward while the rear palm feels as if it is pushing downward and the rear elbow is pulling backward. At the same time the two palm hearts have the feeling as if they are being sucked inward.

The Neck:

The neck is straight (but not tense) with a gentle lift at the back of the neck.

The Chin:

The chin is very slightly tucked down and in.

The Teeth:

The teeth are closed together without force. This is one of the "Three Closings."

The Eyes:

The eyes are level and look straight ahead at the "tiger's mouth." This allows you to focus on what you are doing and puts your head in the correct position.

The Tongue:

The tongue is relaxed and slightly curved, touching the roof of the mouth.

The Breath:

Relax and breathe in and out through the nose. As you stand and relax, you may find you are breathing slower and more deeply. Try to feel your breath sinking into your lower abdomen, into the *dan tian* area. Breathing should be slow, smooth, continuous, even and deep. Breathing into the *dan tian* will help you relax your chest.

Posture Two: "Double Hand" *San Ti Shi*

As stated previously, in the Shanxi style of Xing Yi Quan the "double hand" *san ti* posture is typically assumed during the ending sequence of a form while the "single hand" *san ti* is preformed as part of the opening sequence of a form. This is not only a characteristic of Wang Ju Wu's Xing Yi, other styles from Shanxi Province, such as the Song Shi Rong style, also end their form sequences with this posture.

When practicing these postures in isolation from the forms, in other words, as part of "standing practice" by itself, the practitioner can transition straight from the "single hand" standing posture to the "double hand" standing posture as indicated in the series of photographs starting below and continuing onto the next page.

From the "single hand" *san ti* the practitioner will shift the weight forward and allow both hands to separate out to the sides as shown in photo #2 below. From this position the hands move upward and the weight begins to shift back to the rear leg. Then the practitioner will draw the hands back in along the center line of the body and draw the front foot inward as all of the body weight is shifted to the back leg as shown in photo #3 below. From this position, the front leg steps out as in the "single hand posture" while both hands press downward as shown in photos 4 and 5 on the next page. Notice that both palms are facing downward and the knife edge (small finger side) of the forward hand is facing forward. The rear hand is placed in front of the *dan tian* as in the "single hand" posture. All other body alignment requirements remain as outlined in the last section.

When examining photographs 4 and 5 notice the roundness of the forward arm. The arm should be held in a gentle curve from the small finger all the way up to the middle of the back. In this posture the practitioner is developing a combination of "ward-off" energy and pressing down energy in the forward arm.

Examining the photograph of Wang Ji Wu on page 77, you will notice that he is not pressing downward with the forward hand, but is allowing the forward hand fingers to point downward. This is a more advanced posture. Pressing

Photo #1

Photo #2

Photo #3

Photo #4   **Photo #5**

Photo #6   **Photo #7**   **Photo #8**

down with the palm as Zhang Bao Yang is doing in the photos on the opposite page helps to extend the intention to the palm and fingers. If the beginning student holds his hand as Wang Ji Wu does in the photograph on page 77, the fingers will tend to be limp as the beginning student has not yet developed the proper intention or power in the hands. The beginner should hold the hand as Zhang Bao Yang demonstrates in the two photos on the previous page.

To conclude the standing practice the practitioner will close as shown in the photographs on the bottom of the previous page. First both hands separate out to the sides as shown in photo #6. Next the hands raise up above the head as shown in photo #7, and then the practitioner comes to a resting position as shown in photo #8. The practitioner should stand in this relaxed position for several minutes, breathing naturally and relaxing the entire body.

Chapter 4

Xing Yi Health and Body Strengthening Exercises: An Introduction

Wang Ji Wu with the Xing Yi "Needles"

Xing Yi Health Exercises
An Introduction by Wang Lian Yi*
Translated by Tim Cartmell

The Five Elements, Yin and Yang, inside and outside, intent, qi, power, hard and soft, form and spirit, technique, internal power, false and real, the original yang qi, all united into one.

- Wang Fu Yuan

The way of health involves exercise, nutrition and personal hygiene, all of which enable the individual to enjoy both a healthy body and spirit. In addition, we must also address the issues of preventing and curing disease and the method of extending life.

There are two major influences on the length of life. One is the harmful effects of disease and injury, the other is the natural process of aging. If we wish to be healthy, we must apply the principle of "active use to prevent decay." This involves physical training, internal cultivation and the practice of the Xing Yi Quan health exercises. Following the above method will enable one to strengthen their life energy, prevent illness, delay the aging process and extend life.

Wang Ji Wu is a famous contemporary master of Xing Yi Quan, and is already over one hundred years old. He has benefited greatly from his practices of cultivating the pre-birth *qi* and Xing Yi arts. The master believes in teaching by example, and has taught the complete health art to the public. Master Wang has drawn on his vast knowledge of the internal martial arts, Chinese Medicine, secret teachings, personal experience and one hundred years of training to put together a system of health exercises. This method is the essence of Master Wang's knowledge. The movements are easy to learn, and are suitable for young and old alike. People of both sexes, the healthy and those with physical problems or illness may all practice with great benefit. The Xing Yi health exercises are the very method Master Wang himself practices on a daily basis. This book includes extensive explanations and illustration to present the exercises so they may be easily learned. Many of the concepts presented here have been withheld from the general public as precious secrets.

In addition to thoroughly explaining these concepts, Master Wang has included many of his own discoveries gleaned from a lifetime of dedicated practice. The practicality of the exercises in this book have been proven over time and this method is truly a treasure of the Chinese people. Life is movement.

Actually, the oldest medical treatise in the world, the *Yellow Emperor's Book of Internal Medicine* states, "with movement there is no decay." Why is this so?

The basic processes of life are in metabolic assimilation and breakdown. Assimilation involves processing nutrients taken in from outside the body and

---

* Wang Lian Yi, Wang Ji Wu's son, wrote this material in 1991 while Wang Ji Wu was still alive. This material was published in Wang Lian Yi's book *Shen Gong* in 1992

making them into substances the body can use. These substances become part of the body and are stored as energy. Metabolic breakdown involves taking organic matter inside the body and breaking it down, thereby releasing energy. The processes of assimilation and breakdown involves taking organic matter inside the body and breaking it down, thereby releasing energy. The processes of assimilation and breakdown are mutually supportive and occur without end. When the building process of assimilation is greater than the tearing down of the body through metabolic breakdown, then the body increases its strength. When breakdown is predominate the opposite holds true, the body becomes weaker. Although physical exercise causes metabolic breakdown to produce energy, it stimulates increased assimilation and adaptation to the effort of exercise, which in turn strengthens the body. This is the meaning of "life is movement," the various life support systems of the body are stimulated through exercise.

Health and Training

The muscles of the human body are made up of bundles of muscle fiber which are capable of contraction. Within the muscles are many nerves, blood vessels and glands. As people grow older, the strength of their muscles slowly deteriorates. With regular exercise one may increase the size, elasticity and strength of muscles, improve circulation, stimulate the metabolism, and improve one's speed, endurance, agility, and coordination. With advanced age, one very often experiences calcification of the joints, and weakening of the muscles and connective tissue. With regular exercise, the tenacity of the joints may be increased allowing the joints more elastic strength and freedom of movement, thereby preventing arthritis and stiffening of the joints.

The elderly also often experience a loss of elasticity in the walls of the blood vessels, sometimes causing a loss of efficiency in the pumping action of the heart. Regular physical exercise can help prevent this drop in efficiency by keeping the heart muscle strong, increasing the number of capillaries and the stroke volume of the heart. These benefits of exercise result in a strong heart which in turn is responsible for efficient circulation throughout the entire body with a lower resting pulse rate. The heart will increase in weight and will have more endurance which will enable the individual to handle more stress and responsibility. All of the above benefits add up to protection against many of the problems of old age, such as arteriosclerosis, high blood pressure and many of the other problems that plague those of advanced years.

As far as respiration is concerned, consistent exercise promotes deep and full breathing. The slower and deeper the breath, the fewer breaths taken per minute. This type of breathing allows the respiratory system time to rest. When the respiratory capability is good, the individual is full of vitality and the aging process is slowed.

Regular exercise also aids digestion, stimulating peristalsis and secretion of digestive fluids. Food is broken down and assimilated more quickly. In addition, exercise increases the depth of respiration which in turn causes a greater degree of motion in the diaphragm. This diaphragmatic motion helps to massage the internal organs, including the stomach and intestines which also aids in digestion. Because of these reactions, exercise can help cure stomach and intestinal problems, prolapsis and constipation.

During exercise the circulation of the whole body is increased which stimulates metabolism and can strengthen the liver and spleen. During exercise, the muscles and joints relax and contract in rhythm. This type of rhythmic motion provides a very beneficial stimulation to the brain. The favorable reaction of the brain serves to condition the nervous system, improve its reaction time, reflex speed, preventing fatigue and strengthening resistance.

Exercise is also capable of improving the functions of the kidneys, increasing the kidney's ability to eliminate the waste products of metabolism and absorption of water and necessary substances. The skin also benefits from exercise as circulation is increased, metabolic processes are stimulated, the sensitivity of the skin improves and the amount of resistance to the external environment increases. In addition to the above benefits, exercise also improves the level of functioning of the various glands and stimulates the production of new blood in the bone marrow.

Therefore, if one wishes to enjoy good health and a long life, fit in both body and spirit, then it is necessary to have a regular program of physical training. The value of such exercise has been substantiated by doctors, physiologists, those involved in cultivation of the body, martial artists and history itself. A famous French physician in the eighteenth century once said, "Exercise can take the place of medicine, but all the medicine in the world cannot take the place of exercise."

The contemporary hundred year old master of Xing Yi Quan, Wang Ji Wu says, "Xing Yi Quan, the health exercises of Xing Yi Quan, and the pre-birth method of cultivation have been the treasures that have given me a lifetime of benefits in good health. I have practiced them for nearly one hundred years, and the time has passed as quickly as a day. I have never taken a break from training and my diligence has paid off in a healthy body and spirit, a clear and quick mind and wisdom. My life is proof of the effectiveness of the method, superior to any medicine or drug, as the "medicine" involved in this method of self cultivation is found within oneself and strengthens one from the very root of one's being."

At one hundred years of age Master Wang's state of health is as follows: The functions of his heart and lungs are normal, his blood pressure is normal, his digestion is excellent, his mind is perfectly clear, his eyesight is good, his heart is at peace and he always maintains an optimistic attitude. The above facts are ample proof that the practice of Xing Yi Quan, the health exercises and the pre-birth method of cultivation are an extremely effective system for promoting health and long life. This system may serve as a base for the cultivation of a long, prosperous and healthy life.

The practice of internal martial arts provides tremendous benefits to the nervous system, glands, internal organs, skeletal system, meridians and joints while generally strengthening, balancing and toning one's entire physical self. The effects of exercise in the area of recovery from illness are often more pronounced than the ingestion of drugs. Regular exercise is the best method of strengthening one's physical make-up, improving the body's functions, stimulating metabolism, insuring a long healthy life and actively preventing harm from affecting one's mind and spirit. It is a great pity that so many people still are unfamiliar with the many benefits of exercise and consequently are content to remain as they are. This is a great detriment to society as a whole.

The Dangers of Insufficient Exercise

Because the lifestyle of a great many people neglects regular exercise, ill health is often the direct or indirect result. Although the idea of insufficient exercise as a "disease" is a new concept in the medical field, it is however a very real and serious problem. Physical problems caused either directly or indirectly from lack of exercise usually develop slowly over a long period of time and go unnoticed. When the problem starts to cause obvious physical symptoms it is often too late to effect a cure. Prevention is the most effective method of dealing with these types of illness. Regular exercise will strengthen the body and make it healthy, preventing disease from the inside.

Why does insufficient exercise lead to physical problems? The various systems and organs in the body all have a certain amount of reserve energy over and above the amount typically needed for normal functioning. This reserve can be compared to the backup power reserved for emergency use in machines. For example, a person may survive with only one kidney, and a small portion of the liver is enough to perform the liver's entire function. The heart too has a great deal of reserve capacity. For example, a young person can go through daily life using only fifty percent of the total capacity of their heart. The problems start when the person does not get enough exercise, or the exercise they do get is insufficient to maintain their reserves of energy. The energy the body normally holds in reserve is slowly reduced because of lack of use. As far as the individual is concerned, he or she feels normal and the results of medical examination are also normal. The danger of having no extra reserves of energy for bodily functions only becomes apparent when the individual exerts effort beyond the minimum. For example, the individual may climb stairs or run a few steps to catch a bus, suddenly noticing shortness of breath or a racing heart. Ability to adjust to extremes in temperature and resistance to all types of disease is lowered. Finally, when the body's energy reserves are entirely gone, medical examinations will often uncover problems that could have been prevented and often treatment at this stage is too late.

Modern medicine no longer looks at the absence of obvious disease as the definition of health. Other factors, such as the state and functional capabilities of the organs and physical endurance are taken into account when deciding on the state of an individual's health.

Because change occurs so rapidly in both nature and society in our modern world, people of today have to cope with threats to their health that were nonexistent in the past. For instance, the development of labor saving devices, automobiles, television, industrialization, and increased competition in the work place have all contributed to increasing the stress of life while reducing the opportunity for exercise. Particularly harmful are the disastrous results of insufficient exercise, and this problem deserves special attention.

Physical Labor is Not a Substitute for Systematic Physical Exercise

Here I would like to remind those who still have not made regular exercise a part of their lives, for whatever reason, that the whole issue of maintaining physical fitness goes beyond the individual's personal health and also influences one's family and society as a whole. Everyone should try to participate in an exercise program to enhance their quality of health and life.

There are also those individuals who feel that because their occupation involves some sort of physical labor they do not need to engage in a systematic physical fitness program. This is an erroneous assumption. While it is true that physical labor provides some beneficial exercise, the problem is that the exercise is usually limited to certain muscles or functions, while the rest of the body receives little or no benefit. This is especially true in today's era of specialized labor. The result of specialization is the repeated performance of the same motion over an extended period of time, often resulting in overwork and injury to the overused part of the body. A good example is women involved in weaving textiles. As they are forced to stand all day in a stationary position, they often experience pain in the legs and waist, varicose veins and prolapses. Those engaged in heavy physical labor, such as the loading and unloading of cargo also have problems with pain in the legs and waist and arthritis. Miners often have problems with their joints and lungs. It can be seen from the above examples that there are great differences between the results of labor and a program of systematic exercise. Systematic exercise provides motion for all of the joints and muscles and stimulates the nervous system in a beneficial way, promoting a pleasant calmness while reducing fatigue. Therefore, individuals should choose a program of regular exercise according to their physical condition and needs and begin the process of building a healthy body and spirit.

When reviewing the methods of beneficial exercise, *qi gong* has taken its place along side martial arts and sports in recent years and must not be overlooked. *Qi gong* has attracted the attention of great numbers of people and has had a profound influence on the lives of many. In the areas of improving the people's physical constitution, protecting health, curing illness and extending life, the results of *qi gong* practice have been especially pronounced.

The history of *qi gong* is very long and its sources varied. Buddhists, Daoists, Confucianists, Chinese medical practitioners, martial artists, and the arts of Xing Yi Quan, Tai Ji Quan, Ba Gua Zhang and Shao Lin Quan all have their own theories, methods of practice and special characteristics. Each of these methods contain deep and seemingly mysterious practices at higher levels of training.

In China during the end of the decade of the 1950's and the beginning of the 1960's, the practice of *qi gong* for health, curing disease and prolonging life had already gained acceptance. After two decades of development and promotion by the government, *qi gong* has greatly increased in popularity and its practice has become widespread, most notably in the areas of treating chronic illness, increasing resistance to disease, raising the level of health and strengthening the body. By now people enthusiastically welcome the opportunity to practice *qi gong*. At the same time, the types of *qi gong* and methods of training have "grown as bamboo after the spring rain," with ever increasing popularity.

Master Wang Ji Wu has prolonged his years past his one hundredth birthday and has benefited greatly from the practice of pre-birth *qi gong* and the art of Xing Yi Quan. Based on his life long experience, mastery of the principles and method of Xing Yi Quan and personal insights and breakthroughs, Master Wang has taken into consideration the requirements of the prevention and curing of disease, health and life extension and has developed a method of simple exercise suitable for those of any age or sex, as well as the weak and infirm. Master Wang offers his system of physical cultivation to all people in the hopes that it will improve the health and quality of life of those who practice.

Master Wang Ji Wu combined the elements of Buddhist pre-birth methods of cultivation with the Xing Yi Quan system of internal cultivation and his own precious experience to form a unique system of exercises which, although deep in principle, are easy to practice. The method utilizes natural, abdominal respiration to strengthen the pre-birth original *yang qi*. The result is a method which opens the pathways of blood and energy, increases internal power, rids one of disease and improves the health.

It is important to maintain a cheerful and optimistic state of mind, releasing any concepts that are not conducive to good health, as well as controlling the "seven emotions and six desires." One should keep a quiet and happy heart, allowing the body to remain in its normal state. This will allow one to have a heart as calm as still water, comfortable, and concentrated so that the heart and spirit unite as one. The breath should be natural and smooth with the tongue pressing against the roof of the mouth, the lips gently closed, the eyes looking "inward" and the ears listening to the self, the heart and breath are coordinated and the intent is on the *dan tian*.

From the extreme of stillness, motion is born. When the heart is quiet and the body relaxed, one will come to a state of "emptiness" in which the self is forgotten. In this state, the original pre-birth *yang qi* will fill the body and circulate freely of its own accord. In this state of quiet relaxation, one should practice the Xing Yi exercises for health. The movements should be performed smoothly and rhythmically while adhering to the instructions. Then one will naturally receive the benefits of a long and healthy life.

Xing Yi Quan boxers in Shanxi Province, May 31, 1960

Wang Ji Wu was not the only example of Xing Yi Quan's tremendous health benefits. Pictured above are a group of Xing Yi Quan practitioners in Shanxi Province in 1960. Song Tie Lin (first row, second from left), a student and nephew of Song Shi Rong, lived to be 94 years old. Bu Xue Kuan (first row third from left), a student of Che Yi Zhai, lived to be 96 years old. Li Gui Chang (last row, far right) is currently 82 years old and lives in Taiyuan, Shanxi Province. Li still practices Xing Yi Quan every day.

Wang Ji Wu's son, Wang Lian Yi, writes about his father's health maintenance and body strengthening program
Translated by Tim Cartmell

In the cultivation of life, both movement and stillness are equally important. Master Wang Ji Wu's understanding of Xing Yi Quan is very profound, especially in the area of internal cultivation. His experience is unique. In the practice of Xing Yi Quan's internal exercises, Master Wang has reached the level where the skill has become one with his very self, and his internal power is tremendous. He has come to the state in which "boxing is not-boxing." Of his accomplishments in Xing Yi Quan, the most noteworthy is the set of sixteen health exercises which he compiled from his personal experience. These exercises are the crystallization of the best of the Master's knowledge. If the exercises are practiced diligently, one may eliminate illness, improve the health and extend one's life. Master Wang encouraged the public to study these exercises, as his wish was to contribute to the health and welfare of all. Such is the hope of the master, and the people's benefit has been great.

Regarding the art of Xing Yi Quan, it is not only the practice of form but also possesses a very advanced theory of combat. The fighting techniques are highly refined and flow through changes without end. In addition, the art includes a profound method of internal cultivation which is relatively unknown. In the past, this system of internal exercise was taught only to advanced students of the style, and only after they had reached a very high level in the art. The art of Xing Yi Quan includes methods of both internal and external cultivation, and movement and stillness are seen as equally important. It can be said of the art that the so-called "external" movements are based on the foundation of internal cultivation. With the internal and external in coordination the form and spirit may unite, with the form as the "body" and the spirit as the "use." In the art of Xing Yi Quan the so called external practice should have as its goal the strengthening of the internal, with the accumulation of internal power as the goal. Therefore, Master Wang places equal importance on both internal and external practice and when cultivated in this manner the pristine *yang qi* and the *dan tian* nourishes the whole body. The *qi* will be full and the meridians clear, the blood and *qi* sufficient, the body healthy and the spirit full, resulting in a long and happy life.

Master Wang followed the *Dao*, worshiped the gods and sat in meditation. He practiced the method of cultivating the life force, which proceeds through the practice of boxing, or internal exercise (*qi gong*) in three stages, namely changing essence to *qi*, changing *qi* to spirit and changing spirit to the void. Through this process the strength acquired after birth is replaced by the original, pre-birth strength and the goal of strengthening the life force is realized, resulting in a healthy body and long life.

Master Wang put even more effort into cultivating the original nature. This is achieved through worshiping the gods and meditating at a very high level. It is at this stage the spirit is changed to the void. The Three Treasures acquired after one is born are the essence, *qi* and the spirit. The Three Treasures of one's pre-

95

birth original nature are original *qi* (post-birth *qi* is equivalent to air), spirit, and one's nature. Since the changing of the spirit into void is so important, Master Wang placed special emphasis on this *gong fu*. With the changing of spirit to void the original, pre-birth *qi* fills the body, causing one's intelligence to rise to a higher state, the mind becomes pure and wisdom is the result. If one wishes to see further ahead, one must climb to a higher place. So it is with the cultivation of the original nature; one must cultivate the self continuously over a long period of time, eventually returning to one's original self. The cultivation process can be compared to the refining of steel a hundred times over which in the end is capable of repelling evil for a thousand miles.

Master Wang made use of Xing Yi boxing and the method of cultivating the original essence to open up his internal energy systems, allowing the pre-birth, original *yang qi* to flow unimpeded. This original, pre-birth *yang qi* accumulates in and fills the *dan tian*, strengthening the root of one's life, preventing disease, preserving health and extending life. One often hears the saying: "It is preferable to supplement one's health with food than with medicine, but strengthening one's health by strengthening the spirit is best of all." The principle here is the essence of Master Wang's method.

One should become adept at cultivating the original, pre-birth *yang qi*, thereby preventing invasion by any harmful agents. This original pre-birth *yang qi* is cultivated through the practice of Xing Yi Quan and *qi gong* (the pre-birth method of cultivation). The *qi* then becomes full and is stored in the *dan tian*. The Xing Yi Quan classics state: "Cultivation of the *dan tian* is the treasure of long life, ten thousand catties of gold can never really be possessed by man." Of course, in the cultivation of the *dan tian*, one must have the correct method, practice diligently without a break, "as if ten years passes as a single day." This is the formula for success. Practice and cultivation cannot be separated. One must practice sincerely and cultivate oneself with a focused heart, only then will the treasure of life be preserved. External practice and internal cultivation are of equal importance, even to the extent that oftentimes the internal cultivation is the key to success. One must never forget internal cultivation and only focus on the external practice.

It should be pointed out that external practice and internal cultivation are actually two sides of the same coin. They are developed together and are mutually supportive of the other's growth. The meaning of being adept at cultivation is self evident, it refers to valuing the opportunity to do what is appropriate in a particular situation, putting all one's heart into this cultivation in order to develop the self.

First, one must realize that internal cultivation is a treasure of life. Although this forms the very fiber of one's being, still in order to be made manifest one must accumulate over time. This cultivation of the self cannot be achieved in a short time, but rather requires a lifetime of attentive effort. If one forgets oneself and indulges in that which is harmful, once the damage is done, no amount of money will be able to repair it, moreover, there will be harm to one's health and longevity, great caution is advised. When cultivating the self, besides creating the conditions and environment necessary, one must always seek to protect the original pre-birth *yang qi*, insuring its continued development, living a life of few desires, developing a very deep and powerful internal energy to the utmost degree. At the same time, one must also guard against the invasion by any harmful influences from the outside.

If one remains relatively free of the passions of the senses, harmful outside influences will not be able to affect the self. According to Buddhist thought, the "six senses" which must remain free of desire are the eyes, ears, nose, tongue, body, and mind. One must guard against allowing pernicious influences entering through these sense organs by always maintaining a high level of pure thought. Harmful effects are invariably brought about first through the intellect creating a thought which later becomes the focus of contemplation, finally resulting in the thought becoming actualized in reality. This is the sequence of events which harms the original, pre-birth *yang qi*. As this harm has very serious consequences, one must never treat this type of situation lightly, as to do so is to invite disaster.

One should avoid overindulgence or impulsiveness with regard to the seven emotions: joy, anger, happiness, worry, sadness, fear or surprise. The reason is an excess of any of these emotions influences the tranquility of the heart, causes adverse reactions in the internal organs, impedes circulation, promotes illness and is harmful to the original, pre-birth *qi*.

The essence, *qi*, and spirit are the very roots of life. An excess of sexual activity is harmful to the original pre-birth *qi*. Sexual excess also causes a depletion of the essence and *qi*, which in turn is harmful to the *dan tian*. One must guard against this excess at all costs, in order to prevent disease and prolong life.

One must guard against the harmful influences of the four seasons: coldness, dampness, humidity, excessive heat, and dryness. The harmful effects of the weather can lead to infection by disease which is extremely harmful to the original pre-birth *qi*.

One should make efforts to direct one's thoughts toward opening new channels of useful energy while restricting the waste of mental resources. One should always strive toward strengthening the original pre-birth *qi* and its conservation. The goal is to eliminate all areas which are harmful to or a drain on one's energy resources. This is the method of beneficial cultivation.

There should be order in everyday life and restrictions on food and drink. Only when one's life is orderly and stable is one able to persevere in consistent training. One should guard against disorder in one's schedule. Books, newspapers and magazines should be read on a regular basis.

Before arising in the morning and before sleeping at night there is a set of exercises that will promote health. One should take a "dry bath." The method is to rub the *dan tian*, perineum, *yong quan* points (on the soles of the feet), and the back of the neck*. Upon arising one should rotate the waist, lift the legs and then exercise or practice the elements of Xing Yi Quan. Following this method will increase one's internal strength.

Food and drink should be simple and plain. The protein intake must be adequate but the bulk of food should be low calorie/high nutrition. One should eat foods like fish, vegetables and lentils. Pay attention to cleanliness in choosing and preparing food. Stay away from foods that are sweet, oily or too strong. Never overeat. In winter, it is good to eat some mutton, eggs soaked in Shaoxing wine or sweet rice wine and ginseng chicken soup. One should eat many, small meals a day. Food should be chewed thoroughly and swallowed slowly.

---

* See Xing Yi Exercises Performed Lying on a Bed on page 183

Following the above advice will aid in digestion and assimilation. Again, one must never overeat or overdrink. One must not smoke.

Keep the surrounding environment clean, fee of pollutants and as quiet as possible. The rooms of the house should be clean, airy, sunny, warm but not too hot. It is good to grow plenty of plants in the house and keep fresh air flowing. Clothes should be kept clean, changed often and dried in the sun.

Some examples of individuals whom have practiced this system of health exercise and the results of their practice are listed below:

Wang Xiu is an assistant professor at the Beijing Normal University. He is eighty years old. Mr. Wang studied the Xing Yi sixteen exercise set of health building exercises with Master Wang Ji Wu, practicing daily, all year round without interruption. At eighty Wang Xiu enjoys good health, with none of the health problems commonly associated with old age, such as high blood pressure, heart disease or problems with the internal organs. His eyesight, hearing, mental faculties and memory are all normal. Mr. Wang's digestion is excellent, his appetite good and he is energetic and full of spirit.

Ma Chun Yun is an eighty five year old retired official. Mr. Ma has paid attention to cultivating his health by leading an orderly life, maintaining a positive attitude and remaining active. He practices the pre-birth method of cultivation with pronounced results. He is in excellent health, his eyesight and hearing are very good, he is full of spirit, and he reads and writes every day. Mr. Ma meditates twice a day, quieting his mind and cultivating his original pre-birth *qi*. After each session of meditation he feels comfortable and full of energy. If Mr. Ma feels uncomfortable, or any part of his body is in pain, he uses his time in meditation to circulate his original pre-birth *qi* to the area and experiences immediate relief. He feels the benefits of meditation to be very pronounced and is even more resolute in his daily practice. Ma Chun Yun feels that his practice of cultivating the health through meditation is really a treasure of life.

Liu De Tai is a ninety year old retired government official. After retirement Mr. Liu kept active with daily walks. Later, it was his good fortune to learn the Xing Yi sixteen exercises for health from Master Wang Ji Wu. Mr. Liu practiced the exercises diligently, but found them somewhat difficult at times. He persisted and after a period of training began to feel much stronger. Mr. Liu now walks with a strong step and is full of vigor. Mr. Liu practices the Xing Yi exercises for a half hour every morning, followed by a walk. In the evening he practices the exercises again. In daily life he pays attention to preparing for the weather, eating correctly and taking care of any minor illnesses that may arise. If he ever feels under the weather, he notices after practicing his exercises he will sweat lightly and the discomfort disappears. He rarely needs to take medicine. Mr. Liu believes in maintaining a positive and happy outlook on life, and is careful not to let his emotions have too great an influence on him. He recommends the Xing Yi exercises as they are easy to study, can be practiced at the individual's pace and when matched with breathing are especially beneficial to the elderly. Other advantages of this system are that it requires no preparation and very little space to practice, while the benefits are outstanding. For Liu De Tai, the Xing Yi exercises have become an indispensable part of life.

A Brief Introduction to the Xing Yi Sixteen Health Exercises

by Wang Huan Sheng
edited and revised by Zhang Bao Yang,
Wang Jin Yu, and He Yu Qi
translated by Tim Cartmell

The Sixteen Health Exercises (hereafter referred to as the Sixteen Exercises) were originally called the Xin Yi Liu He Sixteen Movements Internal-External Training (Xin Yi Liu He is also called Xin Yi Quan, Liu He Quan and is presently called Xing Yi Quan and is so named for the remainder of this article). They were developed out of a long period of training in the Xing Yi Quan method. Below is a brief description of their origins, special points, effects, and method of performance.

Origins

Xing Yi Quan is one of the three orthodox internal martial arts (together with Tai Ji Quan and Ba Gua Zhang). Xing Yi Quan specializes in *"gang"* or hard power. The *Xing Yi Quan Canon of Boxing* (hereafter referred to as the *Boxing Canon*) in reference to the sequence of training states: "Those who begin to study must first stand in the *San Ti Shi* posture, and afterwards practice moving forms." *San Ti Shi* is the stance keeping exercise of Xing Yi Quan. The moving forms refers to the Five Elements. These are the basic movements of the art. No matter if one practices the *San Ti* posture or the forms, all must conform to the proper form and method of power unique to Xing Yi Quan, these include: chicken leg, dragon body, bear shoulders, tiger holding head, and the internal and external six harmonies. The *San Ti* posture and the five elements are two sides of the same coin. *San Ti* is the still version of the five elements, the five element forms are the dynamic version of the *San Ti* posture. Together they form the foundation of the art of Xing Yi Quan. Whether standing in *San Ti Shi* or practicing the five elements, one must always concentrate the spirit and *qi*, be relaxed and natural, and never use brute force. From the point of view of the various parts of the body and organs, if one does not concentrate the spirit one will have a high level of nervous tension. Because of this, if one does not take time to perform the necessary preliminary movements which calm the body and prepare it for training, it will be easy to suffer harm. In addition, in ancient times, many practitioners of the martial arts trained not only for health, but also in order to reach a high level of refined martial skill. They often expended a great amount of time in intense physical training. For this type of training, proper preparatory exercises were even more important. The *Boxing Canon*, in reference to the correct method and sequence of training states: "Begin by moving softly, gently and slowly in order to soothe and open the connective tissue and bones, this guides the *qi* and power and leads it correctly. After a period of practice, it is good to use more force and speed in order to increase the internal power for practical application." It is apparent from this passage that the Boxers of previous generations were familiar with the correct sequence of training. The above mentioned sequence of training is in complete accordance with the rules of physical education. Therefore, in the long run correct training is founded on correct performance of basic preparatory movements. Still, many instructors would neglect the preparatory movements. To remedy this situation, Master Wang Ji Wu built on the foundation of the teachings of his teacher, Wang Fu Yuan, and compiled the basic exercises into a set method.

This set of exercises can be practiced alone as a system of health building, or they can be used as a preparatory warm up and post exercise cool down. In addition, these exercises can be used for osteopathic rehabilitation. Several decades of practice have proven their efficacy in the above mentioned areas.

Special Points

1) These movements are based on the basic requirements for Xing Yi power training. Everyone knows that Xing Yi requires one to "hold the chest and stretch the back," "sink the shoulders and drop the elbows," and not to "stick out the chest and lift the stomach." In performance of the Sixteen Exercises these basic principles apply throughout. In the first exercises "Circling the Arms in Front of the Chest," the second exercise "The Jade Dragon Weaves Around the Body," and the third exercise "Opening and Closing Soothes the Meridians" while standing in a horse stance, it is apparent that the chest is held and the back is stretched, etc. But even in the fifteenth exercise "*Yin* Opens and *Yang* Closes," which is a breathing exercise, the same principles still apply.

2) These exercises not only address the external form, they also pay attention to the development of internal power. The two types of training should unite as one. In accordance with the requirement that one should first open the connective tissue and relax the body, some of the movements are to be done with the greatest range of motion possible. The purpose is to open and soothe the joints by moving them through their full range of motion. Although most of the movements of the five elements and twelve forms do not require movement through a full range of motion, still the extra flexibility acquired through the Sixteen Exercises will add to the body's power. Therefore, Xing Yi Quan places great importance on these movements.

Just as the boxing forms of Xing Yi are practiced in single movement forms, so too are the movements of the Sixteen Exercises. Why should movements be performed singly and repetitively? The *Boxing Canon* states "Xing Yi Quan has many single forms, they should be often practiced this way. After a long period of training one will break through and there will be no limit to the depth of skill." It also states: "In defeating others, quality (of technique) is preferable to the amount. In defeating a single opponent this is the method, in defeating many opponent's this is still the method." The principle of "a few things highly refined" was incorporated into martial training. This principle is the same as the

Xing Yi Quan adage to "practice the plain without embellishment, practicing simple movements until they are highly refined."

In addition to simple physical movements, Xing Yi Quan places importance on internal training. The *Boxing Canon* states: "In the martial way, that with a form is the external posture, that without a form is the *qi*/power. That which makes the posture move is the *qi*/power." It is also stated: "If one wishes to practice to the highest level of skill, one must strengthen the *dan tian*, if one wishes to strengthen the *dan tian*, one must first practice technique." Why must one strengthen the *dan tian*? The *Boxing Cannon* continues: "Without strengthening the *dan tian*, the *qi* will not be full, if the *qi* is not full, the strength will be insufficient and the five fists and twelve forms will be empty movements." So, in order to strengthen the *dan tian* why must we first practice technique? Most people believe that if the body suffers no harm it will naturally live to an old age, the *Boxing Canon* says, "but in the end one will not be able to use the power of the *dan tian* unless one practices technique." One must practice both the internal and the external in order to have the "internal and external unite as one, bringing about the unity of the six harmonies."

The Sixteen Exercises also puts great emphasis on the unity of the internal and external and the unity of movement and stillness. One must seek stillness in movement. Stillness dwells in its unity with motion and the "unification of the internal and external." From the point of view of health, these exercises stimulate and regulate the various physiological systems of the body. This conforms with the rule of life, which is "movement." From here there is a balance of *yin* and *yang*, the meridians will be open and the *qi* will be cultivated. If one wishes to acquire these benefits, then there must be a balance of stillness and movement and not an excess in either direction. This is the special point of Xing Yi Quan and also the Sixteen Exercises.

3) This section will discuss the Sixteen Exercises and their basis in "practical use." Everyone is familiar with Xing Yi Quan's practical use, often referring to "vertical and horizontal, advancing and retreating, rising and falling, and rise, drill, fall, and overturn." All of these are interrelated. In practical application, these are united into one body. Here we will not go into detailed explanation. However, we need to be familiar with the basic spirit of these things as they are included in all movement of the Sixteen Exercises. For example, in exercise six "Empty the Foot and Lift a Single Hand," the lifting of the single hand movement also includes the "lifting" and "drilling" components of the boxing skill. In exercise nine "Raising the Back Seven Times," the two palms hanging includes the energy of "tiger pouncing" and "falling and overturning." Exercise twelve "Moving the Hips to the Left and Right," includes the intention of the "brush the water form" of the Swallow Form. It also includes "rising, falling, advancing and retreating."

4) This section will discuss the "system" of the movements in the Sixteen Exercises in relation to exercising the whole body. Although the Sixteen Exercises are composed of single movements, they are all interrelated. From the point of view of the whole body, the exercises work from the top of the body downward. The exercises begin with the arms and head, working down the body to the lower extremities. The first four exercises work primarily the upper body, the fifth through seventh exercises work the trunk and waist, and from exercise

eight on, the lower body is exercised. The entire body is exercised in this set and the instructions are simple to follow. All the various systems of the body are exercised, making this set a complete training for the whole body.

5) The exercises of the Sixteen Exercises set are both adaptable and flexible. As previously stated, the Sixteen Exercises can be practiced singly, as health building exercise, they can also be performed as a warm up for strenuous activity and as a regulating cool down after activity. They can also be used to build the foundation for martial power. Because of this, these exercises are extremely adaptable and versatile. They can be successfully performed by those of different age groups, both sexes, those with different goals in mind and also by those of varying physical condition.

The elderly and infirm can practice the movements according to their abilities. For example, take the horse riding posture in the first exercise, one may squat higher or lower depending on physical ability. The elderly and infirm may bend their knees only slightly while the young and strong or those practicing for the martial arts can squat as low as possible. As another example, in exercise five "The Two Hands Hold Up the Heavens," during the forward bending movement those with high blood pressure or beginners can bend over slightly. Also, the number of repetitions can be limited. In addition, it is not necessary to perform all sixteen exercises in one exercise period. One may choose several and practice only those.

When performing the Sixteen Exercises, the basic requirements include not using brute strength and being natural and relaxed. This is especially suited to the elderly and infirm. Does this mean that the results of practice are not as good for the strong? Quite the opposite. Let's look at the basic requirements for health and strength. We all know that "life is motion," this is a basic principle. If a person exercises on a regular basis he or she will have a strong life force, healthy constitution, and will be full of spirit. The boxing masters of old recognized this principle. In the *Boxing Canon* it is stated: "If one wishes to strengthen the body, any type of martial training will suffice." The reason is no matter the style of boxing chosen, they are all based on movement. Movement is an intrinsic quality of life. Daily exercise equals a healthy body. Besides this, frequent exercise also naturally results in an increase in power and an increase in the elasticity of the body. One may also improve the quality of the exercise, the range of motion of the body and the number of repetitions performed. Especially since one is required to exercise without using brute force (not using force does not mean the body has no constructive stress during exercises, but rather the amount of stress is under conscious control and is always appropriate to the individual's physical condition). This type of exercise improves the physical condition and is suitable for those of all levels of fitness.

6) The Sixteen Exercises do not require any type of equipment. All that is necessary is a small, level space. The exercises are silent and will not disturb those around. One may practice indoors, outdoors, or in a small space like a balcony. This system is convenient, economic and very effective.

Benefits of Practice

The Sixteen Exercises have evolved through over ninety years of practical experience and have been regularly practiced by many students. The results have been the weak becoming strong and many diseases have been cured. These exercises have proven beneficial in treating various chronic diseases, including: high blood pressure, hepatitis, tuberculosis, and neurasthenia. The exercises have also proved helpful in curing injuries involving soft tissue and problems involving the mobility of the joints, such as inflammation and back problems. These exercises are an excellent method of building the health and strengthening the body after injury or illness.

Method of Practice

In discussing the method of practicing the Sixteen Exercises, let's first discuss the old rules passed down from our predecessors. Next we will go over the actual method of training in detail. During exercise, one should follow the basic principles for salubrious exercise.

1) Perseverance: These exercises will increase the health and change one's constitution, but results do not come overnight. After a few days of practice one cannot hope to see great changes. What is called for, rather, is consistent exercise over a long period of time. From the point of view of physiology, it takes time for changes to occur in the various systems and organs of the body, especially in regards to the central nervous system and the ability of the brain to adapt to the stress of exercise. In addition, in learning any skill, it takes a period of time during which the new movement patterns must be repeated before the body assimilates the motion. A period of repetitive practice is required for the central nervous system to have a concrete memory of the sequence of movement. Therefore, practice should be consistent and regular. Even if the movement skills are acquired, if one neglects the exercises for a period of time the skills will be lost. These principles apply to all movement skills and the Sixteen Exercises are not the exception.

If one wishes to see results, the exercises must be practiced consistently and continuously. The *Boxing Canon* states: "In the practice of martial arts, one should be humble, if one stops after a little training or practices on and off, one will never reach a high level of skill." It also states: "If one has no perseverance, studies a little and thinks they understand much, feels satisfied with their level of skill, studies sporadically, or thinks they are an expert, one will find in application they are useless, this is not the fault of the teacher but of the student." These passages are an accurate description of the result of sporadic training.

2) The proper sequence of training: When studying anything, one proceeds from the simple to the complex and from the easy to the difficult. Martial training is no exception. One should especially take heed in regards to the amount of exercise taken. The ability of the body to endure increasingly greater levels of stress in exercise increases gradually. During the practice of the Sixteen Exercises, one must gradually build upon one's current level of fitness by increasing the amount of exercise the body can accommodate. Exercising within one's level of fitness while gradually increasing the difficulty will steadily improve the physical condition. This builds the foundation for complicated and difficult exercise. These principles are in accordance with the physiological laws of exercise and established methods of scientific training. To exercise in opposition to these principles will not only be ineffectual but also may be harmful.

3) Complete development: The Chinese medical point of view of the body as a "wholistic entity" is scientific in nature. The development, or lack thereof, of any part of the body has an effect on all other parts. Underdevelopment in one area will interfere with the development of all other parts. Therefore, exercise should be composed of various movements. This is conducive to the overall development of the whole body. With even development of the whole body comes the potential for a high level of skill and fitness. The Sixteen Exercises pay special attention to this point. For example, exercise twelve "Moving the Hips to the Left and Right," in which you squat on one leg to the left and right and exercise thirteen and fourteen are all interrelated. The range of motion of various exercises all have a mutual effect on the other.

4) As a warm up or cool down: When practicing martial arts, before standing in the *San Ti* Posture and walking through the forms one should first warm up. After training one should cool down and regulate the body. After exercise it is advisable to perform various cool down movements which regulate or "work out" any tension that may have accumulated during training. These movements should relax the whole body. Cool down exercises also prevent any adverse reactions from suddenly stopping intense exercise.

Important Points For Practice

1) The form and spirit must be relaxed: The *Emperor's Classic of Internal Medicine* states: "When the emotions are empty and weak, then the *qi* flows, when the spirit is held within, disease will not come." The term "weak emotions" refers to having a relaxed and natural spirit. One must maintain a relaxed composure. We are all familiar with the great influence the emotions have on the health, we do not need to go into it here. Having a relaxed body means to avoid using brute strength. The body and spirit are both natural and relaxed. The two may then unite as one. This will lead to an increase in internal power, as well as health. This state is the beginning of the healing process. Relaxed does not mean slack. It means to remain natural in the midst of exertion, never straining. This relaxed state will release both accumulated mental and physical fatigue. After a period of training, one will have a radiant spirit and powerful movements.

2) The breathing matches the movements naturally: The principle is to inhale when doing stretching and opening movements. Like exercise nine "Raise the Back Seven Times," or exercise fifteen "Yin Opens and Yang Closes," when raising up or opening the hand outward one should inhale deeply. When performing closing movements, then exhale. Like exercise five "The Two Hands Uphold the Heavens," or exercise ten "The Two Fists Strike the Back," or exercise Thirteen "The White Crane Rotates its Knees," when bending forward, returning the hands or squatting down, one exhales. When there are moves which involve both stretching and contracting simultaneously, the rule is to breathe naturally and never force or hold the breath.

3) Maintain good living habits: Exercise aids in promoting health. But if one has poor living habits in general, one will still be unable to realize the goal of good health. Everyone knows this to be true. For those who practice the Sixteen Exercises, whether for the prevention of disease or to cure an existing ailment, without a regulated lifestyle, a sensible diet and an appropriate amount of exercise, one will be unable to improve health. A sensible lifestyle and proper exercise however, will allow one the benefits their heart desires.

4) Other points:

a) Practicing in an area with fresh and circulating air is ideal. One should avoid drafts, especially when perspiring.

b) Before practice it is advisable to empty the bladder and bowels. During exercise, the internal organs receive a high degree of stimulation. Going to the rest room before practice one may avoid any discomfort during training. In addition, the movements of the organs will not be obstructed. Xing Yi Quan places great importance on the exercise of the internal organs. The *Boxing Canon* states: "The five organs must function smoothly." The five organs are the heart, liver, spleen, lungs, and kidneys.

c) Before practice one should not be too hungry nor too full. If one is too hungry, there will be a lack of energy, if one is too full the stomach may be injured.

d) Always maintain a calm heart, never talk or joke during training, in order to prevent scattering the spirit.

e) After practice, do not immediately eat or drink, nor lie down, in order to avoid disturbing the digestion and flow of *qi*.

During Practice is a Teacher's Guidance Necessary?

Finally, let's discuss whether or not it is necessary to have a teacher, and if the student can accurately learn the Sixteen Exercises alone. The answer to these questions cannot be generalized. We must analyze the questions according to the applicable principles. The *Boxing Canon* has this to say: "For those practicing the martial arts, eighty percent of the time is spent training alone, twenty percent with another. It takes a long period of time to strengthen the self and a short amount of time to defeat an opponent." It is also stated: "When considering strengthening the body, it is not important which style of martial arts is chosen, all will serve this purpose." Here the principle is clearly stated, the first goal of martial arts is to strengthen the body and any method of martial arts training is acceptable. The reason is that all martial arts involve "movement," and movement is the root of life.

Movement is an essential quality of life. The only consideration is whether or not the movements conform to correct posture and are systematic. When choosing a method of exercise, one should consider personal training goals and one's own physical condition. If the goal is a healthy body, relaxed and comfortable exercise which avoids the use of brute strength is all that is required. If one perseveres in practice, benefits naturally accrue. If one wants to train not only for health but also for martial ability, then besides adhering to the principles of relaxed exercises which avoid brute strength, one must also pay close attention to performing the movements in strict form. For those only interested in health, following the written directions is sufficient. But for those who wish to train for martial ability, it is best to practice under a teacher's guidance. Always remember this: as long as one practices in a relaxed manner without using brute strength the exercises will naturally conform to the correct principles of movement. Here one must examine the self. Many people have the same kind of feeling after practicing the exercises, that is, they feel comfortable and relaxed as if they had just taken a bath. This is evidence that the practice is correct and that the principles are being correctly followed.

Chapter 5

Wang Ji Wu's
Body Strengthening and
Health Maintenance
Exercises

Editor's Introduction
by Dan Miller

The material in this chapter is a combination of written material taken from Wang Lian Yi's book *Shen Gong* and material provided by Zhang Bao Yang, Wang Jin Yu, He Yu Qi, and Wang Huan Sheng. The presentation of each exercise follows the same format; there is an introduction, followed by practical information on how to perform the exercise, followed by a "song" explaining the exercise. The introduction and the "song" were written by Wang Lian Yi in his *Shen Gong* book. The practical information about how to practice the exercise was provided by Zhang and the others mentioned above.

You will find that the information provided by Zhang's group is very direct and practical while the information by Wang Lian Yi is at times uses terminology from Chinese medicine. We provide both of these explanations as we feel it will help the reader better understand the full depth of the exercises. You will notice that many of the exercises have two titles, the first title listed is Wang Lian Yi's title, the second title is that used by Zhang Bao Yang's group.

At first glance this exercise set may appear to be very similar to any other *qi gong* or *nei gong* set of exercises one may have encountered while studying the internal martial arts. However, Wang Ji Wu's genius in putting this particular set of exercises together is in the set's completeness as an internal development system. This set of exercises was not put together haphazardly. There is a completeness and wholeness in its design and at the same time this set of exercises is simple, practical, easy to learn, and easy to execute.

Any internal development exercise set should consist of exercises which serve to integrate the body, mind, and breath while strengthening the body energetically, viscerally, and physically in a natural and balanced manner. Energetically, the set should contain exercises which are designed to calm the mind and body so that energy sinks to the *dan tian*. In addition, the movements should distribute that energy in a full and balanced fashion throughout the body through gentle coaxing. The movement of energy should not be forced through the use of strong intention or muscular tension. The mind is calm and the physical movement gently urges the movement of the *qi*. As Wang Lian Yi states in his introduction to exercise number four, "Wang Ji Wu felt that the beginner should not try and force the *qi* to flow through strong intention. His advice was to practice the exercises with a relaxed mind and the intention focused on the *dan tian*. After the *qi* has gathered in the *dan tian*, it will find its own way in the "Small Heavenly Cycle" through the gentle coaxing of the physical movements." The energy movement exercises in Wang Ji Wu's set are designed to move energy to all distal points of the body in a natural, balanced, and safe manner.

Another important component in any complete internal development system is visceral manipulation, or simply stated, motion designed to move each of the visceral organs to a small degree so that the organs are gently massaged and thus there is less chance for fluid stagnation. In the last chapter Wang Lian Yi stated "life is movement." Everyone knows that if any part of the body remains stationery for an extended period of time, it becomes stiff. If muscles, tendons, and ligaments are not moved through their full range of motion on a regular basis the individual will start to loose that full range of natural, unrestricted motion. A well designed set of exercises will be devised so that all of the body's joints, muscles, tendons, and ligaments are moved through their full range of motion during the exercise set. Wang's set does this, but additionally some of this set's exercises work to gently move and manipulate the internal organs so that the organs function properly and all of the systems of the body which pump fluids are stimulated. When bodily fluids such as lymph, bile, blood, etc. are allowed to stagnate anywhere in the body, problems will arise. In order to prevent stagnation, the body needs to bend, move, and stretch so that no small "pools" of fluids are allowed to collect and become stagnant. Wang Ji Wu's set of exercises is expertly designed to work all of the viscera so that the organ energy is stimulated and the bodily fluids are encouraged to move freely.

In terms of physical development, this set of exercises not only gently stretches the muscles, joints, ligaments, and tendons to keep them operating optimally through their full range of motion, it also helps to build the type of whole body, coordinated strength which is functional in the internal martial arts.

Exercise One: Uniting the Original *Qi*
(Circling the Arms in Front of the Chest)

Introduction: The state of an individual's health can be said to be determined by several factors, including heredity, external factors (food, weather, etc.), one's state of mental health, the environment, one's attitude toward life, etc. Under further analysis, such influences as environmental factors and internal factors, such as the emotion, combine to form complex patterns of influence on one's health. But from the point of view of medicine, physiology, cultivation of the health and the Xing Yi Quan method of exercise, the state of one's *qi* is the primary consideration.

According to (Chinese) medical science, the basic theories of *Yin/Yang* and the Five Elements hold that in the natural world, physical forms must interact with *qi* in order to create; movement and stillness must follow one another if the things of creation are to develop, and the state of personal health is determined by the condition of the *qi* and blood. "*Qi* is the leader of the blood, blood is the mother of *qi*." When the *qi* and blood are "sufficient" the body is healthy. According to the theory of Xing Yi Quan's internal and external methods of cultivation and training, the original "pre-birth" *yang qi* is the very root of that which protects the health. Therefore, in preserving and building health the cultivation of *qi*, strengthening of the *dan tian* and refining the essence until it transforms into *qi* are most important.

The main purpose of this first exercise lies in regulating the breath, cultivating the *qi*, and breathing with the *dan tian* as the root of the breath, thus allowing the original *qi* to circulate freely throughout the whole body. When the *qi* is sufficient the spirit is full, and one may prevent illness, cure disease, improve and strengthen the physical constitution, raise the level of health and extend the life.

Preparatory Posture

110

Preparatory Posture: Stand up naturally, the heels together, the toes point outward at a 60 degree angle (see photo 1-1). The whole body is relaxed and comfortable, do not stand stiffly, the eyes look straight ahead, close the mouth, the tongue touches the roof of the mouth, breathe naturally, imagine the breath moves in and out of the *dan tian*, concentrate the spirit and quiet the *qi*. Now you are prepared for movement.

Method of Practice:

1. Open the legs, the feet point straight ahead and are parallel, the feet are shoulder width apart, slightly bend the knees. This is usually called "squatting in the horse riding stance" but here the purpose and emphasis is different. You must hold the chest naturally, stretch the back (lengthen the spine) and gently lift the anus. See photo 1-2.

2. Lift the hands to the front with the palms facing outward (photo 1-3).

3. Move the hands to the left side (photo 1-4). Move very slowly. Continue, moving the hands down in front of the body, the palms will naturally face inward as the hands move down (photo 1-5). Continue moving the hands toward the right side (photo 1-6). Return the hands to the starting position (photo 1-7). Continue moving the hands to the left, downward, to the right and then back up (photos 1-3 through 1-7). Continue making circles with the arms in front of the body.

4. After completing a number of repetitions, reverse the direction of the circle and repeat for the same number of repetitions (photos 1-8 through 1-11).

Number of Repetitions: One should perform the exercise according to one's physical condition. Those who are weak or ill, or who have just begun to exercise, can practice fewer repetitions. The strong can practice more repetitions. As the physical condition improves, one may increase the number of repetitions from eight to sixteen to thirty two or even more if one desires.

Important Points:

1. The arms must not be stiff as if using strength, and must not be bent too much. Bend the arms at a natural angle.

2. The fingers are slightly spread apart and the palms are rounded.

3. Relax the shoulders.

4. Breathe naturally. At the top of the circle, begin to exhale, at the bottom begin to inhale.

5. While moving, as an aid in concentrating the spirit, one may silently count the

number of repetitions.

6. Move slowly. Imagine that your hands are moving through water.

The Range of Motion and Effects:

The main purpose of this exercise is to condition the shoulders. The muscles of the arms are also exercised. This exercise is structured around contracting the upper arm inward then extending it outward, the arms are twisted in and out. These motions provide a complex movement which involves the trapezius muscle, latissimus muscle, the pectorals, the biceps, the triceps, and the muscles of the forearms. Therefore, this exercise can be used in conjunction with medical treatment as an aid in curing problems with the shoulders, arms, and back.

For martial arts this exercise is very good for developing the *jing* (trained strength) required when deflecting to the side or blocking in a downward or upward motion.

Photo 1-1　　　　**Photo 1-2**　　　　**Photo 1-3**

Photo 1-4　　　　**Photo 1-5**　　　　**Photo 1-6**

Photo 1-7

Photo 1-8

Photo 1-9

Photo 1-10

Photo 1-11

Photo 1-12

Photo 1-13

113

The "Song" of Uniting the Original Qi:

The body stands naturally erect, the two arms are relaxed, hands at the sides.
Concentrate the spirit and quiet the *qi*, close out interfering thoughts as much as possible.
The heart is as still as water; heaven and earth exist together.
The eyes look straight ahead, the limbs and body are relaxed.
The mouth is closed, the tongue touches the roof of the mouth.
The *qi* and breath fill the arteries, circulating to and from the "sea of *qi*."

The feet are opened parallel, in the horse riding posture.
The entire soles of the feet grip the ground, the "bubbling springs point" is contracted inward.
The knees are bent, the energy of the waist moves downward.
The palms are placed on the tops of the thighs, the fingers are stretched and opened.

Relax the shoulders and empty the chest, press the head upward and straighten the back of the neck.
The intent is kept in the *dan tian*, the breath is delicate, inhale gently.
Exhale smoothly, delicately, even, slow, and long.
Press up the sky and stand erect on the earth, one *qi* complete and natural.

The two arms extend forward, moving from the shoulders.
Bend the elbows and lift the palms, bend them at a natural angle.
From the left to the right, make a circle in front of the body.
Moving in continuous circles, circling around in a turning motion.
At the top of the circle, begin to exhale, at the bottom begin to inhale.
The energy comes from the *dan tian*, from the shoulder to the elbows.
The elbows push the palms and hands, the power reaches the four extremities.

From right to left, make a circle in front of the body.
Moving in continuous circles, circling around in a turning motion.
At the top of the circle, begin to exhale, at the bottom, begin to inhale.
Focus on the three heart centers, the center of the palms, the center of the feet, and the center of the body.
Relaxing all of the joints, the power reaches the four extremities.

The *qi* and breath move in and out, the *dan tian* expands and contracts.
The *qi* follows the movements of the palms, the palms move and the *qi* goes.
The spirit and form unite as one, the intent first leads, it moves through a complete cycle and then returns, in cycles without end.
The *qi* is full and the spirit concentrated, when the spirit is concentrated the heart is at peace, the fire and water are united, the kidneys are strengthened and the skill is refined.

Exercise Two: The Jade Dragon Weaves
Around the Body
(Pulling Horizontally Right and Left)

Introduction: In this exercise the two palms move as if they are in the clouds. The palms are held about five inches apart, the *yang* hand overturns and the *yin* hand supports. The jade dragon suddenly appears, his body swimming through space, the *qi* and power follow one another, the heart with the intent, the intent with the *qi* and the *qi* with the power, these are the three internal conditions. Use the intent to lead the *qi*, the *qi* to move the power and the power to move the hands and feet. The *qi* follows the movements of the external form, the form goes and the *qi* moves, the form and *qi* are sensitive to one another, the ten thousand things are created. *Yin* and *Yang* are united, the five elements must follow smoothly, the extreme of stillness contains the intent to move, movement and stillness unite as one, the *qi* is stored in the *dan tian*, from there it may be issued externally.

Preparatory Posture: The horse riding stance. See photos 2-1 and 2-2.

Method of Practice:

1. Bend the elbows and extend the arms to the left side (photo 2-3).
2. The left hand is at the height of the left armpit, the left palm faces upward.
3. The right palm is in front of the chest, with the palm facing downward.
4. Slightly round the palms as if the hands are grabbing something (like a large rope). The distance between the hands is about four or five inches, pull the hands to the right, level with the ground (photo 2-4).
5. As the right hand passes the right armpit, turn the palm to face upward, the left palm simultaneously turns to face palm down. The right hand passes the right armpit and the left hand is in front of the chest (photo 2-5). Continue, pulling the hands back across in front of the chest toward the left (photos 2-6 and 2-7).
6. Continue the exercise by pulling the hands back and forth in front of the chest (photos 2-3 through 2-8).

Number of Repetitions: Start with eight repetitions back and forth. Increase the number to sixteen and eventually to thirty-six or more.

Important Points:

1. When pulling the hands horizontally left and right, extend and bend the arms naturally, do not stiffen the arms. In addition, imagine you are actually pulling something from left to right.
2. As you are pulling, the hips will naturally turn a little to aid in the motion, but do not swing the hips intentionally.
3. The shoulders remain relaxed.

The Range of Motion and Effects: This movement is also primarily an exercise of the shoulders. The arms move, one rotating outward while the other twists inward, the range of motion is somewhat greater than that of exercise one.

| **Photo 2-1** | **Photo 2-2** | **Photo 2-3** |

Photo 2-4

Photo 2-5

Photo 2-6

Photo 2-7

Photo 2-8

Photo 2-9

Photo 2-10

The "Song" of the Jade Dragon Weaves Around the Body:

The body stands up straight, the hands are hanging beside the body.
Calm the heart and quiet the *qi*, no thoughts, no cares.
Look straight ahead, the spirit is held within.
Close the mouth, the tongue touches the roof of the mouth.
Regulate the breathing, in and out from the *dan tian*.

The feet are opened parallel, a bit wider than the shoulders.
Stand in the horse riding posture, bend the knees.
The energy of the two knees is as if they are moving towards each other without actually moving, the two feet feel as if they are twisting inward.
The *qi* sinks to the *dan tian*, the perineum is gently lifted.

Relax the shoulders and empty the chest, press the head up and straighten the back of the neck.
Press up toward the sky and stand erect on the earth, one *qi* complete and natural.
The intent is kept in the *dan tian*, the intent leads the *qi*.

The left arm extends out straight to the left front, at the height of the chest.
The palm of the left hand faces upward, relax the shoulders and sink the elbows.
The right arm also extends out to the left, to the right of the left arm.
The distance between the left and right palms is about 4-5 inches, the right palm faces the ground.
One hand faces up and the other faces down, one should imagine one is stroking something, the energy is the same as "cloud hands."
Move from the left to the right, the energy of the hands coordinate and the hands move through a level plane, to the right side.
The elbows are naturally bent, the shoulders are relaxed and opened.

After the hands have move to the right front, the right hand turns palm up, the left hand turns palm down, the left palm is to the left of the right palm.
The palms are about 4-5 inches apart.
The hands move from the right to the left through a level plane, moving to the left side.
The hands move to the left and right, in cycles without end.

   Yin and *Yang* are united, the *qi* moves to the *dan tian*, the shoulders are relaxed and the elbows sink, the palms feel as if they are pulling a thousand pounds, the waist and hips, the hands and feet, the intent and the *qi* are all connected, the internal organs are solid and the life is prolonged.

Exercise Three: Opening and Closing Soothes the Meridians (Circling the Arms to the Front and Back)

Introduction: The joints, meridians and skeletal frame serve the functions of allowing the body mobility. Practicing the Xing Yi Quan Exercises for health will keep these various systems in excellent condition, preventing aging and loss of mobility while promoting cellular metabolism which preserves the capabilities of youth; supple muscles, quick reactions, and great vitality for life.

Preparatory Posture: The horse riding stance. See photos 3-1 and 3-2.

Method of Practice:

1. The right palm presses against the left armpit. The four fingers are under the armpit, the thumb is outside against the front of the shoulder. The palm presses against the center of the left chest muscle (photo 3-3).
2. The left hand makes a fist, the shoulder is relaxed, the elbow is comfortably extended (photo 3-3).
3. The left fist moves from hanging straight down and begins to lift up toward the front (photo 3-4), it continues circling over the top and down towards the rear, making a complete 360 degree revolution (photos 3-5 through 3-7). After making a certain number of repetitions, reverse the direction of the circle (photos 3-8 through 3-10).
4. Change arms and repeat circling the right arm in the forward and reverse directions (photos 3-11 through 3-20).

Number of Repetitions: Make the same number of repetitions with each arm in both directions. One may start with eight repetitions and slowly increase the number over time.

Important Points:

1. The shoulders must not be rigid
2. Bend the arms a natural amount.
3. Do not use power.
4. Imagine there is some resistance around the wrists and hands.

The Range of Motion and Effects: This exercise is a combination of bending and straightening the arms as well as moving the arms in a circular motion. As the range of motion of the shoulder is great in this exercise, it is a good exercise for those who have stiff shoulders.

Photo 3-1

Photo 3-2

Photo 3-3

Photo 3-4　　　　Photo 3-5　　　　Photo 3-6

Photo 3-7　　　　Photo 3-8　　　　Photo 3-9

Photo 3-10　　　　Photo 3-11　　　　Photo 3-12

Photo 3-13   Photo 3-14   Photo 3-15

Photo 3-16   Photo 3-17   Photo 3-18

Photo 3-19   Photo 3-20   Photo 3-21

The "Song" of Opening and Closing Soothes the Meridians:

The body stands naturally erect, the hand beside the body.
Concentrate the spirit and quiet the *qi*, the heart is calm as still water.
Close out interfering thoughts as much as possible, the spirit is held within.
The eyes look straight ahead, the body is relaxed.
Close the mouth, the tongue touches the roof of the mouth.
The *qi* and breath fill the arteries, circulating to and from the *dan tian*.

The feet are opened parallel, slightly wider than shoulder width.
Adopt the horse riding posture, the entire soles of the feet grip the ground.
Bend both knees, the "bubbling spring point" is contracted inward.
The palms are on the tops of the thighs, the fingers open and extend.

Relax the shoulders and empty the chest, press the head up and straighten the back of the neck.
The intent is kept in the *dan tian*, inhale delicately.
Exhale smoothly, the breath fine, even, slow and long.
Press up toward the sky and stand erect on the earth, one *qi* complete and natural.

Place the right palm on the top of the left ribs, the hand and elbow are pressed firmly against the front of the chest.
The left hand makes a fist, with the shoulder joint as the axis begin moving the left arm in complete revolutions.
From the bottom to the front, from the front to the rear, swing the arm freely in a circle.

Place the left palm on top of the right ribs, the hand and elbow are pressed firmly against the front of the chest.
The right hand makes a fist, with the shoulder joint as the axis, begin moving the right arm in complete revolutions.
From the bottom to the front, from the front to the rear, swing the arm freely in a circle.
Relax the shoulder and ease the elbow, the movement matches the circulation of *qi* and breath.

This movement can help open and stimulate the meridians, exercise the joints, increase the circulation, aid digestion, open the stomach, increase the peristalsis of the intestines, increase the absorption of nutrients, increase the resistance to disease, breakdown and elimination of wastes and increase the overall health of the body.

Exercise Four: Ju Que and Xuan Wu
Divide the North and South
(Clapping the Palms Above and Below)

Introduction: Traditional Chinese Medicine, Xing Yi Quan, pre-birth methods of cultivation and practical experience all hold the following to be true: The state of an individual's health is directly influenced by the fullness or lack of original pre-birth *yang qi*, and the condition of the *qi* and blood. If the *qi* and blood are in good condition then the body is healthy. Of utmost importance is the state of the original pre-birth *yang qi*; if it is "full," strong and circulates freely throughout the body then the health of the body is positively effected.

This exercise is particularly helpful in stimulating the flow of *qi* through the meridians, especially in the *Ren* and *Du* meridians. If the *qi* circulation in the *Ren* and *Du* meridians is strong, the "Small Heavenly Cycle" is open and there are great benefits to health, including increased metabolic activity, increased resistance to disease, increased powers of recovery from illness and leading to a long and healthy life.

While *qi* circulation in the *Ren* and *Du* meridians is a vital part of maintaining health, Wang Ji Wu felt that the beginner should not try and force the *qi* to flow through strong intention. His advice was to practice the exercises with a relaxed mind and the intention focused on the *dan tian*. After the *qi* has gathered in the *dan tian*, it will find its own way in the "Small Heavenly Cycle" through the gentle coaxing of the physical movements.

Preparatory Posture: Stand naturally, the feet are together (photo 4-1).

Method of Practice:

1. The two arms hang by the sides. Lift the hands forward and up to a height just above the top of the head and clap the two palms together. Inhale deeply as you execute this move (see photos 4-1 through 4-3).
2. Continuing, the two arms swing down to the rear and clap the hands behind the back. Clap the hands as high as possible behind the back. Exhale. See photos 4-4 and 4-5.
3. Continue clapping the hands above and behind.

Number of Repetitions: Start by clapping above and behind sixteen times, increasing as one's physical condition improves.

Important Points:

1. It is very important to keep the shoulders relaxed. Let the breath match the movement naturally.
2. The arms are naturally straight, one must not hold the arms rigid.

The Range of Motion and Effects: This exercise involves a great range of motion to the front and rear. This exercise, along with exercises one, two, and three can be considered together as a set of exercises primarily for the shoulders. Those with problems of the shoulders, back and hands may use these exercises as treatment.

Photo 4-1

Photo 4-2

Photo 4-3

Photo 4-4

Photo 4-5a

**Photo 4-5b
(side view)**

Photo 4-6

The "Song" of Ju Que and Xuan Wu Divide the North and South

Stand erect, with the hands hanging at the sides.
Calm the heart and quiet the *qi*, close out interfering thoughts as much as possible.
The eyes look straight ahead, the spirit is held within.
Close the mouth, the tongue touches the top of the mouth.
Regulate the *qi* and breath, moving in and out of the *dan tian*.

The feet are comfortably held together.
Adopt a naturally erect posture, slightly bend the knees.
The energy of the knees feels as if they are gently pulled together, the feet close inward.
The *qi* sinks to the *dan tian*, the perineum is gently pulled upward.

Relax the shoulders and empty the chest, press the head up and straighten the back of the neck.
Press up toward the sky and stand erect on the earth, one *qi* complete and natural.
The intent is on the *dan tian*, the intent guides the *qi*.

The two arms move forward and up.
The two palms clap together over the head.
At this time, relax the shoulders, the arms are parallel, breathe in deeply.

Swing both hands down from above to the front and then back to the rear, clapping the palms together behind the back.
At this time relax the shoulders and shock with the arms, exhale completely.
Repeat as many times as comfortable.

127

Exercise Five: Uphold the Heavens
and Firm the Root
(The Two Hands Uphold the Heavens)

Introduction: According to the theories of Chinese medicine, the internal body includes the six *yin* organs and six *yang* organs including the triple warmer. The triple warmer is not a single organ but rather a complex of interactions regarding accumulation and dispersion of metabolically generated heat and body fluids via the thoracic cavity, abdominal cavity, and pelvic or lower abdominal cavity. The triple warmer has no concrete organ and therefore cannot be observed during an autopsy, but can only be known by observing its function in the living body.

In the medical treatise *Lin Qu Ying Wei Sheng Huei Pien* it is written, "The upper warmer is like fog, the middle warmer is like foam, the lower warmer is like a ditch." In the *Medical Recipes for the Internal Organs*, it says, "The classics say the upper warmer is like fog, there the spirit of harmony of original *qi* steams forth; the middle warmer is like foam, this is the center for the digestion and absorption of food; the lower warmer is like a ditch, it is the route for the removal of waste products." From the above it can be seen that the upper warmer functions to disseminate the protective *qi*, the middle warmer functions in absorbing nutrients, nurturing the blood and supplying the entire body with the nutrients it needs, and the lower warmer functions in absorbing liquids and excreting urine and feces.

This exercise involves lifting the hands and bending the waist. This will improve the digestive and absorptive functions of the triple warmer, especially the digestive capabilities of the stomach and intestines and the ability of the bladder to rid the body of wastes. The ability to digest and absorb food, as well as eliminate waste products can all be improved. This in turn will strengthen the physical constitution and promote health and a long life.

Preparatory Posture: Stand naturally, the feet together (photo 5-1).

Method of Practice: This exercise is practiced in two parts.

Part One

1. Interlace the fingers in front of the body, the palms face down (photo 5-2).
2. Lift the palms up along the front of the body, at the same time, turn the hands to face palms up. Extend the arms until the hands are straight up over the top of the head (photo 5-3).
3. Lean the upper body backward as far as possible, then continue by leaning to the left and right, the hands initiate the motion and guide the body to lean left and right. Lean back, left and right three times each way (photos 5-4 through 5-6).
4. Now bend over forward and let the hands move down to the front. The palms touch the ground in front of the feet (photo 5-7).
5. The feet are together with the knees straight, continuing, slightly turn the waist to the left and press the palms down in front of the left foot, now turn the waist to the right and press the palms down in front of the right foot (the fingers are interlaced throughout). See photos 5-8 through 5-10.
6. Stand up and again lift the palms up and straighten the arms with the palms over the top of the head. Repeat steps 1 - 5 three or four times (photos 5-2 through 5-10).

Part Two

1. Bend the arms with the palms facing in with the hands held in front of the forehead. At the same time, take a step forward with the left foot and bend the leg while straightening the right leg into a left bow and arrow stance (photo 5-11).
2. Turn the body to the left and look to the rear, look back and down at the right heel, at the same time the hands can help the body twist to the left (photo 5-12).
3. Turn back to the front and withdraw the left leg, step out with the right foot into a right bow and arrow stance, turn the waist to the right and look back and down to the left heel (photos 5-13 through 5-17).
4. Repeat part two of this exercise twice to the left and right.

Number of Repetitions: The number of repetitions suggested above is the minimum amount. One may increase the number as one is able. Those who are weak or infirm may lessen the number of repetitions.

Important Points:

1. When standing in the bow and arrow stance, the rear heel must not leave the ground, the foot should be flat.

2. Since this exercise places comparatively greater amount of stress on the whole body, one should be especially careful not to use force. In the beginning, if one is unable to perform the exercise as described, do not try to force the movements, competency will come with time.

3. The breathing should be natural.

The Range of Motion and Effects: The first part of the exercise, the forward and backward bending, will stretch out the back and abdominal muscles. As the arms lead the body to stretch side to side, the waist and stomach are strengthened. Not only are the muscles of the abdomen and waist strengthened, the internal organs are also exercised, including the kidneys and major blood vessels in the abdominal cavity.

Part two of the exercise stretches and contracts the intercostal muscles and exercises the lumbar region.

Photo 5-1

Photo 5-2

Photo 5-3

Photo 5-4

Photo 5-5

Photo 5-6a

Photo 5-6b (side view)

Photo 5-7

Photo 5-8

Photo 5-9

Photo 5-10

Photo 5-11

Photo 5-12

Photo 5-13

Photo 5-14

Photo 5-15

Photo 5-16

Photo 5-17

Photo 5-18

Photo 5-19

Photo 5-20

The "Song" of Uphold the Heavens and Firm the Root:

Stand erect with the hands hanging at the sides.
Calm the heart and quiet the *qi*, close out interfering thoughts as much as possible.
The eyes look straight ahead, the spirit is held within.
The mouth is closed, the tongue touches the roof of the mouth.
Regulate the *qi* and breath, moving in and out of the *dan tian*.

Interlace the fingers, place the hands in front of the lower stomach.
The palms face downward, the energy of the arms hangs down.
Turn the palms to face upward, raise the arms and lift them as if holding up the sky.

The power comes from the shoulders and arms, relax the shoulders and lean the waist back.
Return to pressing straight up to the sky, now lean the body to the left side.
Lean the body alternately to the right and left three times.
Breathe out slowly, breathe in smoothly.
(note: This movement stimulates the stomach by providing even pressure all around and strengthens the upper warmer.)

Bend at the waist and straighten the arms, slowly bend forward to the ground.
The hands are still interlocked, press the palms to the ground in front of the feet.
Turn the body to the left, touch the ground outside the left foot.
Turn the body to the right, touch the ground outside the right foot.
Continue the exercise as long as comfortable.
(note: This movement stimulates the bladder by providing even pressure all around and strengthens the lower warmer.)

Extend the left foot forward, move it out a step.
The front leg is bent, the rear leg is straightened.
The hands are interlocked, raise the hands above the head.
The palms face upward, twist the body to the left.
Look back at the right foot, the power comes from the inner thighs.

Extend the right foot forward, move it out a step.
The front leg is bent, the rear leg is straightened.
The hands are interlocked, raise the hands above the head.
The palms face upward, twist the body to the right.
Look back at the left foot, the power comes from the inner thighs.
(note: This movement stimulates the middle of the abdomen and central part of the body by providing even pressure all around and strengthening the middle warmer.)

Exercise Six: Empty the Foot and Lift a Single Hand

Balancing *Yin* and *Yang*, regulating the Five Elements, refining the essence into *qi*, *qi* into spirit and spirit into the void are all traditional theories of Chinese medicine, and Xing Yi Quan internal cultivation practices, and are supported by practical experience. Practicing this set of exercises can increase one's internal power, cultivate the body, increase vitality, slow the aging process, cure disease and extend life. Practicing these movements with intent can balance the internal systems, aid the functions of the organs, strengthen the muscles and sharpen the senses. The transformation of the essence into *qi* builds up the "protective *qi*" which surrounds the body and wards off illness. The internal circulatory systems are regulated, the individual cells are enlivened, the blood is nourished and the *qi* will be full. The nervous system is strengthened, the stomach and intestines are strengthened and digestion is improved. The liver and spleen are benefited and the production of blood is increased. The entire skeletal system receives benefit.

This exercise can be said to be a marvelous method of cultivating the body and improving the health. Those who wish to strengthen the body must look here! The best medicine in the world is inside your own body, all that is lacking is the practice and refinement to make use of it. No matter the reason one has not taken advantage of the healing power of the body before, whether it be ignorance of the correct method, laziness, disbelief or insufficient motivation, now that the method is known, all that is needed is to put the method into practice in order to build health, cure disease and prolong life.

Preparatory Posture: Stand naturally, the feet are together (photo 6-1).

Method of Practice:

1. Slightly bend the left knee, the left foot is flat on the ground. Shift the entire weight of the body onto the left foot.

2. Lift the heel of the right foot off the ground. The ball of the right foot lightly touches the ground.

3. At the same time, bend the elbows and lift the hands until the palms are in front of the chest, the left hand is against the body, palm facing down, the right palm is outside the left palm facing palm up (photo 6-2).

4. The left hand presses downward past the left side of the stomach and hip, at the same time, the right hand pushes upward past the forehead. Do not completely extend the arms (photos 6-3 and 6-4).

5. Continuing, put the right foot down flat, shift the weight to the right foot and lift the left heel with the left toes lightly touching the ground.

6. At the same time, the right hand presses downward, turn the palm to face down, move the hand along the body, the left palm turns palm up and moves up outside the right palm, the left palm lifts up as the right palm presses down (photos 6-5 through 6-8).

7. Repeat with one palm pressing up as the other presses down.

Number of Repetitions: Practice eight times to the right and left to start, gradually increasing to sixteen repetitions.

Important Points:

1. When pushing one hand up and the other down, inhale. When changing, exhale. One may also just breathe naturally.

2. Imagine some resistance when pushing the palms but use no external force.

The Range of Motion and Effects: The upward and downward pressing motions of the palms and the lifting of the heel flex and extend the muscles and joints of the hands, wrists, and feet. Shifting the weight from foot to foot also helps improve balance. The actions of the hands stretch the muscles at the sides of the body and the movement is also beneficial to the peristalsis and digestion.

Photo 6-1

Photo 6-2

Photo 6-3

Photo 6-4

Photo 6-5

Photo 6-6

Photo 6-7

Photo 6-8

Photo 6-9

Photo 6-10

Photo 6-11

The "Song" of Empty the Foot and Lift a Single Hand

Stand naturally, the arms hang by the sides.
Concentrate the spirit and quiet the *qi*, the heart is calm as still water.
Close out interfering thoughts as much as possible, the spirit is held within.
The eyes look straight ahead, the body is relaxed.
Close the mouth, the tongue touches the roof of the mouth.
The *qi* and breath fill the arteries, moving in and out of the *dan tian*.

Move the weight to the left foot, empty the right foot, the ball of the right foot lightly touches the ground.
Regulate the *qi* and breath, the intent encompasses the entire universe.
As from ancient times, heaven and man are one.
The body is agile, reach as if for the sky.

The left arm bends at the elbow, the left hand is held palm open.
Move the hand up past the stomach, the hand stops above the chest.
The center of the palm turns inward, fill the palm with *qi*.
Move the right hand in the same manner, moving to the right side of the body.
Continuing, turn the palm, swing the right palm up as the left palm is lowered.
The left hand is at the left side, the palm facing downward.
The *qi* moves into the palm, the intent is as if pressing down the earth.

The right arm bends at the elbow, the right hand is held in a palm.
The palm faces inward, the *qi* fills the palm.
The left palm is moved to the left side.
Continuing, turn the palm over, lift it up past the chest.
The hand moves up to the height of the top of the head, the palm faces upward.
The *qi* fills the palm, the intent is as if lifting up the sky.

The weight is moved to the right foot, the left foot is empty, the ball of the foot lightly touches the ground.
Regulate the *qi* and breath, the intent encompasses the entire universe.
As from ancient times, heaven and man are one, the body is agile, reach as if to touch the sky.

The right arm bends at the elbow, the right hand is held in a palm.
Move the hand up past the stomach, the hand stops above the chest.
The center of the palm turns inward, fill the palm with *qi*.
Move the left hand in the same manner, moving to the left side of the body.
Continuing, turn the palm, swing the left palm up as the right palm is lowered.
The right palm is at the right side, the palm facing downward.
The *qi* moves into the palm, the intent is as if pressing down the earth.

The left arm bends at the elbow, the left hand is held in a palm.
The palm faces inward, the *qi* fills the palm.
The right palm is moved to the left side.
Continuing, turning the palm over, lift it up past the chest.
The hand moves up to the height of the top of the head, the palm faces upward.
The *qi* fills the palm, the intent is as if lifting up the sky.

Exercise Seven (Part One): Concentrate the Spirit and Gaze at the Heel
(Lean, Tilt, Look Right and Gaze Left)

Introduction: Concentrate the spirit to quiet the heart, the heart is quiet and without interfering thought, without worry. This is the state of *Wu Ji* (無極) the original void. All is united into one, dim and indistinct, returning to the great void, tranquil and flowing endlessly, the large and small heavenly cycles flow naturally, strengthening the kidneys and the essence, nourishing the core of the body, benefiting the brain and nerves, fire and water are balanced, the route of the *dan tian* is open. The internal and external are cultivated together, movement and stillness follow one another, the intent moves and form follows, the form relies on the changes of the intent, be diligent in cultivation and practice, return to that which is natural, the heart is quiet and the intent is true, it is like polishing gold or filing steel into a needle, study diligently with a quiet mind. Once the method is realized, one will enjoy long life, with boundless happiness.

138

Exercise Seven (Part Two):
The Golden Cock Eats Rice

Introduction: According to the traditional theories of Chinese Medicine, besides the "precious" organs, the body also has a network of meridians which run throughout the entire body. Altogether there are twelve main meridians which are connected to the internal organs and are divided into twelve systems. Six of the meridians are *"yang"* and are located along the lateral surface of the body. Six of the meridians are *"yin"* and are located on the medial surface of the body. Because the twelve meridians are connected to and nourish the important internal organs, their condition is most important to the health of the body.

The goal of health exercises and internal cultivation is to cause the original pre-birth *yang qi* to flow freely through the meridians. The *qi* leads the blood, together they nourish all the organs and prevent disease, and increase one's vitality. The cavities that lie along the meridians are important junctures in the flow of energy. The state of these cavities plays a significant role in the prevention of disease. The practice of the Xing Yi exercises for health can stimulate the flow of the original pre-birth *yang qi* through the meridians, helping to remove any obstructions in the cavities thereby greatly improving the health. The benefits of this exercise include comfortably extending the spine and nerves which run to and from the brain, as well as opening the important cavities which lie along the spine, increasing the flow of energy in the *Ren* and *Du* meridians, increasing the life energy, relieving fatigue and calming the spirit while benefiting the brain.

Preparatory Posture: Stand naturally, the feet are together (photo 7-1).

Method of Practice: This exercise is divided into two parts.

Part One: Concentrate the Spirit and Gaze at the Heel
1. The eyes look straight ahead, slowly turn the head to the left, looking back as far as possible, as if looking over the left shoulder at the heels (photo 7-2).
2. Repeat the movement turning the head to the right (photos 7-3 and 7-4).
3. Repeat turning the head left and right and looking back at the heels (photos 7-1 through 7-4).

Part Two: The Golden Cock Eats Rice
1. Lean the head back as far as possible and look up (photo 7-6).
2. Look down as far as possible (photo 7-7).
3. Repeat leaning the head back then bending the head forward.

Number of Repetitions: Repeat according to your physical condition. Those with high blood pressure, or who become dizzy, can start with just a few repetitions and gradually increase the number.

Important Points:

1. During the exercise, one should remain as quiet and concentrated as possible. Move slowly to avoid becoming dizzy.
2. When tilting the head forward the chin touches the chest.
3. Breathe naturally.

The Range of Motion and Effects: This is primarily an exercise for the head and neck. The actions of this exercise work the muscles of the head and the cervical vertebrae, the circulation to the head is increased. The movements help relieve mental fatigue and relieve tension in the central nervous system, while improving its function. In addition, since the eyes look back as far as possible, the muscles around the eyes are strengthened. The exercise is beneficial for those with problems in the head, neck or central nervous system. The muscles of the neck and cervical vertebrae remain healthy and the exercise will also help restore balance to those with high blood pressure or hardening of the arteries.

Photo 7-1

Photo 7-2

Photo 7-3

Photo 7-4

Photo 7-5

Photo 7-6

Photo 7-7

Photo 7-8

The "Song" of Concentrate the Spirit and Gaze at the Heel

Stand erect, the hands hang at the sides.
The heart is calm as still water, there is not the slightest disturbance.
The eyes look straight ahead, the spirit is held within.
The mouth is closed, the tongue touches the roof of the mouth.
Regulate the *qi* and breath, moving in and out from the *dan tian*.

Turn the head and neck to the left, slowly and gently.
Gaze at the heels, the intent moves first.
Concentrate the spirit on the backward gaze, focus on the heels.
The intent and *qi* move together, the energy will flow through the *Ren* meridian.

Yin and *Yang* are united, the energy flows through the heavenly cycles.
Slowly and gently, the intent and *qi* move in an uninterrupted flow.
The head returns to the central position, the *qi* is contained on the *dan tian*.

Turn the head and neck to the right, slowly and gently.
Gaze at the heels, the intent moves first.
Concentrate the spirit on the backward gaze, focus on the heels.
The intent and *qi* move together, the energy will flow through the *Ren* meridian.
The energy flows through the heavenly cycles.

The movement is soft and gentle, repeat as many times as is comfortable.
The *qi* and breath flow comfortably, this exercise prevents dizziness.

The "Song" of The Golden Cock Eats Rice

Stand erect, the hands hang at the sides.
The heart is calm as still water, without the slightest disturbance.
The eyes look straight ahead, the spirit is held within.
Close the mouth, the tongue touches the roof of the mouth.
Regulate the *qi* and breath, moving in and out of the *dan tian*.

The head is held up with the neck straight, relax the shoulders and empty the chest.
The feet grip the ground, the "bubbling spring" point withdraws upward.
Sink the *qi* to the *dan tian*, the perineum is contracted upward.
Move the crown of the head backward, the chin moves upward.
Slowly inhale, breathe into the "sea of *qi*."

Return the head to the upright position, proceed slowly.
The heart is calm and the *qi* smooth, you must not hold the breath.
The eyes look forward, relaxed, quiet and natural.

The head is held up with the neck straight, relax the shoulders and empty the chest.
Sink the *qi* to the *dan tian*, the perineum is gently contracted upward.
Move the crown of the head forward, the "jade pillow" (a point at the base of the skull) moves upward.
Slowly exhale, the air leaves the "sea of *qi*."

Exercise Eight: Ape Arms Enliven the Blood
(Rubbing the Palms)

Introduction: The Chinese medical treatise *Ben Zang Pian* states, "The meridians are the pathways of *qi* and blood, they manage *yin* and *yang*, nourish the tendons and bones and benefit the joints." The meaning of this is the internal organs, bones and joints are nourished by the flow of *qi* and blood. A balanced flow of *qi* and blood also benefits the connective tissue, bones and skin. The balances of the body are all dependent upon this flow. If there are no obstructions to the normal flow of *qi* and blood throughout the entire body, all parts of the body will be nourished and will function normally. The body is then able to ward off harmful influences and maintain its health.

In the *Ling Qu: Theory of Regulating the Meridians* there is a discussion of the "liver storing blood." This refers to the liver's ability to store and regulate the amount of blood it contains. The various diseases of the blood are caused by the "inability of the liver to store blood."

The purpose of this exercise is to open the meridians, including the Twelve Main Meridians and the Eight Extra Meridians, allowing the energy to flow unimpeded. The blood vessels too are opened and the circulation is strong. With the *qi* and blood circulating normally, all the various organs and systems of the body receive the nutrients needed for optimal health and prevention of disease.

Preparatory Posture: Stand naturally, the feet are together (photo 8-1).

Method of Practice:

1. Bend the knees slightly, shift the weight to the right foot, lift the left heel and lightly touch the ground with the ball of the left foot.
2. Bend the left elbow, lift the left hand until it is level with and in front of the left side of the forehead.
3. Put the fingers of the right hand together, rub the left palm in an up and down motion with the right fingers (photo 8-2).
4. Turn the head and look to the right, as if looking at the right heel.
5. After rubbing the left palm a number of times, put the left foot down, shift the weight to the left foot, bend the knee slightly and touch the ball of the right foot lightly on the ground. Lift the right palm and rub with the left fingers (photos 8-3 and 8-4).
6. Repeat to the left and right.

Number of Repetitions: Perform twice on the right and left sides. Rub the palm until it is warm.

Important Points:

1. The shoulders must be relaxed, the arms must not be rigid.

The Range of Motion and Effects: This exercise will increase the endurance of the arms and fingers. It is especially beneficial to those who have injured their hands or fingers. Rubbing the palm stimulates the *Lao Gong* point (in the center of the palm). This is beneficial to those suffering from "heat" in the internal organs, extreme thirst, nasal problems, inability to focus the attention and stroke.

Photo 8-1

Photo 8-2

Photo 8-3

Photo 8-4

Photo 8-5

The "Song" of Ape Arms Enliven the Blood

Stand erect, the hands hang down by the sides.
The heart is calm as still water, without the slightest disturbance.
The eyes look straight ahead, the spirit is held within.
Close the mouth, the tongue touches the roof of the mouth.
Regulate the *qi* and breath, moving in and out of the *dan tian*.

Empty the left foot, the ball of the left foot lightly touches the ground.
The weight of the body is on the right foot.
The intent is on the *dan tian*, the perineum is gently lifted up.

Bend the left elbow, lift it past the stomach to the height of the chest.
Lift the left palm, place it beside the left side of the head.
The center of the palm is at the height of the forehead, as if you are holding up
the sky.

Bend the right elbow slightly, lift the right palm.
Lift it to the height of the head, place the right fingertips against the left palm.
The right fingers rub the left palm, rub with an up and down motion.
Turn the head to the right, look at the right heel.

Empty the right foot, the ball of the right foot lightly touches the ground.
The weight of the body is on the left foot.
The intent is on the *dan tian*, the perineum is lifted upward.

Bend the right elbow, lift it past the stomach to the height of the chest.
Lift the left palm, place it beside the left side of the head.
The center of the palm is at the height of the forehead, as if you are holding up
the sky.

Bend the left elbow slightly, lift the left palm.
Lift it to the height of the head, place the right fingertips against the right palm.
The left fingers rub the right palm, rub with an up and down motion.
Turn the head to the left, look at the left heel.

Repeat as long as comfortable.

Exercise Nine: Raising the Back Seven Times

Introduction: When one is able to lead the breath, the original pre-birth *yang qi* can ensure that the nourishing *qi* flows freely through the meridians, the blood circulation will be complete and each part of the body will receive the nourishment it needs. The organs will then function normally, the body will be healthy and disease will have no place to take hold. At the same time, when breathing correctly one may also fill the *dan tian* which strengthens the internal organs.

This exercise will strengthen the function of the lungs, improve respiration, vital capacity and stimulate metabolic activity. Practicing rhythmic breathing also improves the function of the heart, strengthens the blood vessels, and increases the heart's power of endurance which promotes health and a long, healthy life.

Preparatory Posture: Stand naturally, the feet are together (photo 9-1).

Method of Practice:

1. Lift the hands up in front to the height of the head, the palms face outward.
2. At the same time, raise up on the toes, the legs are together and the knees are straight. The entire weight of the body is on the balls of the feet. Inhale deeply. See photos 9-2 and 9-3.
3. Lower the heels as the two arms drop straight down in front of the body, bend the knees and slightly squat (dropping the body weight and the arms swiftly as the heels are lowered), exhale thought the mouth with the "HA" sound (photo 9-4).
4. Immediately raise up on the toes again and swing the arms up above the head (photos 9-5 and 9-6).
5. Repeat steps 1-4.

Number of Repetitions: Start with seven repetitions, work up the number of repetitions as you are able.

Important Points:

1. The whole body is relaxed. Match the breath with the movement. Inhale when raising up on the toes and exhale when lowering the heels. Remember to exhale through the mouth with an audible "HA" sound.
2. Perform the exercise slowly.

The Range of Motion and Effects: This exercise stretches the muscles of the four extremities, with the matched breathing there is a slight shock when the heels drop, which is good for the internal organs. The exercise is related to exercise five and has a similar effect. In addition, since the entire weight of the body is supported by the balls of the feet, the balance is improved.

Photo 9-1   Photo 9-2   Photo 9-3

Photo 9-4   Photo 9-5   Photo 9-6

Photo 9-7   Photo 9-8

The "Song" of Raising the Back Seven Times:

Stand erect, the hands hang at the sides.
The heart is calm as still as water, without the slightest interference.
The eyes look straight ahead, the spirit is held within.
Close the mouth, the tongue touches the roof of the mouth.
Regulate the *qi* and breath, moving in and out of the *dan tian*.

The *qi* sinks to the *dan tian*, the perineum is gently lifted upward.
Lift the hands together, slowly raise them up over the head.
The two palms face the front.
At the same time raise up on the balls of the feet, the heels raise up off the ground.
Inhale deeply, the point of power is in the feet, arms, waist and hip.

The two arms forcefully swing down.
The heels lower to the ground, exhale with a "ha" sound.
All of the stale air in the lungs is exhaled with the "ha" sound.
This cleans the lungs and benefits the brain, strengthens the heart and improves the liver.

Remember in your heart,
Repeat the exercise, seven times is ideal.
All illness and disease will disappear.

Exercise Ten: Both Fists Strike the Back

Introduction: The *Ren* meridian runs along the front of the body and regulates the *yin*, it is the "sea" of the *yin* meridians. The *Du* meridian runs along the back and controls the *yang*, it is the "sea" of the *yang* meridians. When the *Ren* and *Du* meridians are united and the *qi* and breath flow freely in continuous cycles, then the body will be strong and full of vitality. When the energy flows unimpeded through the *Du* meridian, the *yang qi* of the kidney will rise to the "well of the shoulders" and will flow downward to the heels. The kidney *qi* will be full, the spirit pure and concentrated, the waist and legs will be strong, the internal organs will be at ease. With continued practice of this exercise the results will become obvious.

Preparatory Posture: Stand in the horse riding stance (photo 10-2).

Method of Practice:

1. Close the hands into loose fists, bend the elbows and swing the hands upward. Use the "tiger's eye" (the radial side of the fist) to strike downward on the tops of the trapezius muscles.
2. At the same time, push out the stomach and lean back (photos 10-3 through 10-5).
3. The fists fall back to their starting position hanging by the sides (photos 10-6 and 10-7).
4. Repeat steps 1-3.

Number of Repetitions: Sixteen repetitions is average, one may work up to twenty four or more.

Important Points:

1. When striking the back and pushing out the stomach, inhale. When returning to the upright position and dropping the fists, exhale.
2. After completing exercise nine, one may rest a brief period before beginning exercise ten. Exercise nine is a bit more stressful and one should allow the body time to calm down and become quiet before going on to exercise ten, in order to avoid loss of breath.

The Range of Motion and Effects: This exercise conditions the muscles of the stomach and waist. When pushing out the stomach the abdominal muscles are stretched, this influences the internal organs. The light tapping on the trapezius muscles is beneficial to those who have injured their neck, shoulders, or back.

Photo 10-1

Photo 10-2

Photo 10-3

Photo 10-4

Photo 10-5

Photo 10-6

Photo 10-7

Photo 10-8

Photo 10-9

The "Song" of Both Fists Strike the Back:

Stand up naturally, the hands hang beside the body.
Concentrate the spirit and quiet the *qi*, close out interfering thoughts as much as possible.
The heart is calm as still water, the heaven and earth exist together.
The eyes look straight ahead, the limbs and body are relaxed.
Close the mouth, the tongue touches the roof of the mouth.
The *qi* and blood fill the arteries, moving to and from the "sea of *qi*."

The feet are opened parallel in the horse riding posture.
The entire soles of the feet grip the ground, the "bubbling springs" points are contracted upward.
The knees are bent, the energy of the waist moves downward.
The palms are placed on the tops of the thighs, the fingers are stretched and opened.

Relax the shoulders and empty the chest, press the head upward and straighten the back of the neck.
The intent is kept in the *dan tian*, the breath is delicate, inhale gently.
Exhale smoothly, delicately, even, slow, and long.
Press up the sky and stand erect on the earth, one *qi* complete and natural.
The shoulders and elbows relaxed, close the fists tightly.

The shoulders "urge" the elbows, the elbows "urge" the hands.
Wave the two fists, swing them upward.
Swing them above the head, then down the back.
The fists strike the "well of the shoulders" the chest and waist lean back.
The *qi* and breath move in and out, regulating the movement.

Repeat in this manner, striking the "well of the shoulders."
Continue as long as is comfortable.

Exercise Eleven: Rotating the Waist Strengthens the Kidneys

Introduction: According to the theories of traditional Chinese medicine, the functions of the kidneys include the removal of wastes and uric acid, and also reproduction. In the *Su Xing: Ling Lan Mi Dian Lun* it is written, "The kidney is an organ which gives strength, it makes one clever." The meaning of "giving one strength" refers to energy and vitality, while "making one clever" refers to having a sharp mind. Although the brain is responsible for thought, the cerebral fluid is produced by the kidneys, therefore the health of the kidneys is closely related to one's mental powers.

The kidneys are related to the element water. The ancients believed water is *yin*, however, *yin* is contained within *yang*, this means that there is fire in the midst of water. Because of this, the two kidneys are divided into the water kidney and the fire kidney, the left kidney is water and the right kidney is associated with the *ming men* point and is fire. The functions of the two kidneys are coordinated, when they function together in harmony the body is able to maintain a state of

great vitality. Therefore, the health of the kidneys is very important to the overall health of the body. Practicing the Xing Yi health exercises, especially this exercise, can greatly improve the strength and function of the kidneys resulting in increased vitality, good health in general, a sharp mind and the energy to succeed in life.

Preparatory Posture: Stand in the horse riding stance (photo 11-2).

Method of Practice:

1. Put the hands on the sides of the waist, the thumbs are forward under the front of the lower ribs and the four fingers are on each side of the back near the lumbar region (photo 11-3).
2. Turn the waist in a circle first to the left, then to the front, then to the right, then to the rear (making a clockwise circle). See photos 11-3 through 11-7.
3. After a number of repetitions, reverse the direction of the circle and repeat (photos 11-8 through 11-11).
4. Repeat steps 1-3.

Number of Repetitions: Start with eight or sixteen repetitions and gradually increase the number.

Important Points:

1. The movement should be light and slow.
2. The size of the circle can vary according to one's physical condition.
3. The feet remain flat on the ground throughout the movement. Only the hips and waist should move.
4. Do not let the head rotate or swing, try to keep the head relatively still.
5. The hands should firmly hold the waist. This helps protect the waist muscles and also helps one perform the exercise.
6. Breathe naturally.

The Range of Motion and Effects: This exercise moves the waist, hips, knees, and wrists through uncommon angles of motion. The waist is the central axis of the body's motion, the muscles of the waist and abdomen as well as the kidneys will be stimulated by this exercise. The movement is beneficial for those with pain in the waist.

Photo 11-1

Photo 11-2

Photo 11-3

Photo 11-4   Photo 11-5   Photo 11-6

Photo 11-7   Photo 11-8   Photo 11-9

Photo 11-10   Photo 11-11   Photo 11-12

The "Song" of Rotating the Waist Strengthens the Kidneys

The body stands naturally erect, the hands hang at the sides.
Concentrate the spirit and quiet the *qi*, close out interfering thoughts as much as possible.
The heart is calm as still water, heaven and earth exist together.
The eyes look straight ahead, the limbs and body relax.
Close the mouth, the tongue touches the roof of the mouth.
The *qi* and breath fill the arteries, moving in and out of the "sea of *qi*."

The feet open out parallel, adopt the horse riding posture.
The entire soles of the feet grip the ground, the bubbling well point is contracted upward.
The knees are bent, the energy of the waist moves downward.

The hands are held palms open, place the palms behind the back.
Put the palms on the lower back on each side of the spine, the tips of the fingers should be touching.
The *qi* sinks to the *dan tian*, the *qi* and breath are natural.
Lean back, the stomach moves forward, move the waist in a circle.
Rotate from the front to the left, from the left to the rear.
From the rear to the right, from the right back to the front.
Repeat as long as is comfortable.

Lean back, the stomach moves forward, move the waist in a circle.
Rotate from the front to the right, from the right to the rear,
From the rear to the left, from the left back to the front.
Repeat as long as is comfortable.

Exercise Twelve: Moving the Hips
to the Left and Right

Introduction: The frame, torso, waist and hips are involved in the overall motion capabilities of the body, these areas must not be neglected during exercise. From the point of view of physiology, and the structure of the body, the frame, torso, waist and hips include many important meridians, organs and vital areas of circulation. The importance of these areas should be considered when executing exercises to strengthen the overall functions of the body.

After practicing the Xing Yi exercises for health, one will strengthen the very root of the self, making the body healthy, the *qi* full, the limbs agile, the waist and legs strong, the lower body stable, movements adroit, the steps light, the back straight and the body light and agile.

Preparatory Posture: Spread the legs to double shoulder width apart, the feet are parallel.

Method of Practice:

1. The upper body leans forward, the hands grasp the ankles.
2. Squat down on the left leg, the left knee presses against the chest, the left foot remains flat on the ground. The right leg is stretched straight. Now the waist, back and hips are all turn toward the right side. The eyes look toward the right (photo 12-1).
3. Relax the shoulders, sink the elbows, the palms reach toward the right foot and alternately reach forward and pull back (photos 12-1 through 12-4).
4. Repeat, squatting down on the right leg (photos 12-5 through 12-8).
5. Repeat the exercise twice on each side.

Number of Repetitions: If one has sufficient endurance, more repetitions may be performed if desired.

Important Points:

1. Breathe naturally.
2. For beginners or those who are unable, if one cannot perform the exercise as described, do not force it. Over time one will eventually be able to do the exercise completely.
3. The exercise is to be done slowly, with stability and in a quiet manner. Squatting for longer periods will relax the tendons and increase flexibility, this is preferable to adding repetitions.

The Range of Motion and Effects: In this exercise the upper part of the leg rotates outward to a great degree. The weight of the body is borne by the hip. At the same time, the knees, waist and ankles are also conditioned. With the pushing and pulling motions of the hands, the whole body is exercised.

Photo 12-1

Photo 12-2

Photo 12-3

Photo 12-4

Photo 12-5

Photo 12-6

Photo 12-7

Photo 12-8

The "Song" of Moving the Hips to the Left and Right:

Stand up naturally, the hands hang by the sides.
Concentrate the spirit and quiet the *qi*, close out interfering thoughts as much as possible.
The heart is calm as still water, heaven and earth exist together.
The eyes look straight ahead, the limbs and body relax.
Close the mouth, the tongue touches the roof of the mouth.
The *qi* and blood fill the arteries, moving in and out of the "sea of *qi*."

The feet are opened parallel, the feet are opened comfortably, slightly wider than shoulder width.
The entire soles of the feet grip the ground, the "bubbling spring point" (*yong quan*) is contracted upward.
The ankles are bent, relax the hips.

Squat down on the left leg, the buttocks sit on the left heel.
The knee touches the chest, the torso remains erect.
The right leg is pulled straight and is level with the ground, the entire sole of the right foot remains on the ground.
The ankles are bent, the eyes look at the right foot.

The left hand grabs the top of the left foot, the right hand grabs the top of the right foot.
The head, neck, waist, and shoulders twist to the right.
Sink the elbows and relax the shoulders, the palms push toward the right side.
The *qi* and breath move in and out, follow what is natural.

Squat down on the right leg, the buttocks sit on the right heel.
The knee touches the chest, the torso remains erect.
The left leg is pulled straight and is level with the ground, the entire sole of the left foot remains on the ground.
The ankles are bent, the eyes look at the left foot.

The right hand grabs the top of the right foot, the left hand grabs the top of the left foot.
The head, neck, waist, and shoulders twist to the left.

Exercise Thirteen: Pressing on the Knees
Regulates the Meridians
(The White Crane Rotates its Knees)

Introduction: The meridians, ligaments, and tendons connect and control the skeletal system, waist, legs, arms and hands. The meridians and connective tissue, when healthy, maintain a certain degree of flexibility, elasticity, and tenacity. They allow the body to move with agility and the body is in a fine state of health. With regular exercise, the limbs and body will be strengthened, the functions of the internal organs improved, the original pre-birth *yang qi* will be cultivated and the entire body will benefit. In this state the spirit will be strong, the body healthy and free of disease and one will live a prosperous life.

Preparatory Posture: Stand naturally with the feet together (photo 13-1).

Method of Practice: This exercise is performed in two parts.

Part One
1. Lean the upper body forward, the hands are placed on the knees (photo 13-2).
2. Bend the knees and rotate the knees to the left in a counter clockwise circle (photos 13-3 through 13-6).
3. After a number of repetitions, reverse the direction of the circle. Perform the same number of revolutions clockwise (photos 13-6 through 13-10).

Part Two
1. Return to position number one described above (photo 13-10).
2. Squat straight down until the heels press against the buttocks and the knees press against the chest (photo 13-11).
3. Stand up and repeat step 2 for a number of repetitions (photos 13-10 through 13-12).

Number of Repetitions: Start with eight repetitions and gradually increase the number.

Important Points:

1. Breathe naturally.
2. The knee is one of the most complex joints in the body, its range of motion is small, try to rotate the knees through the greatest range of motion possible, however, do not force the movement in part one. Be careful not to allow the knees to extend laterally beyond a comfortable range of motion.

The Range of Motion and Effects: The main purpose of this exercise is to strengthen the knee joint. At the same time, the feet and ankles as well as the supporting muscles of the legs are also conditioned.

Photo 13-1

Photo 13-2

Photo 13-3

Photo 13-4   **Photo 13-5**   **Photo 13-6**

Photo 13-7   **Photo 13-8**   **Photo 13-9**

Photo 13-10   **Photo 13-11**   **Photo 13-12**

The "Song" of Pressing on the Knees Regulates the Meridians:

Stand naturally erect, the hands hang beside the body.
Concentrate the spirit, close out interfering thoughts as much as possible.
The heart is calm as still water, heaven and earth exist together.
The eyes look straight ahead, the limbs and body relax.
Close the mouth, the tongue touches the roof of the mouth.
The *qi* and blood fill the arteries, moving in and out of the "sea of *qi*."

The entire soles of the feet grip the ground, the "bubbling springs" points are contracted upward.
Bend the knees forward, to about a 90 degree angle.
The hands are placed on the knees, the hands tightly grip the knees.

The hands help support the knees, the knees make revolutions.
From the front to the left, from the left to the rear.
From the rear to the right, from the right back to the front.
The feet remain flat on the ground, they must not raise up.
Continue making circles as long as is comfortable.

Exercise Fourteen: Strengthening the Meridians by Rubbing the Knees and Stretching the Body

Introduction: Transforming the essence into *qi*, the *qi* into spirit and the spirit into the void are the three important steps of the art of Xing Yi Quan. It can be stated that these steps are the method of improving the health, strengthening the body, slowing the effects of aging and extending life. Once one has reached the level of transforming the spirit into the void, the pre-birth *qi* will become refined to the highest degree, filling the body with energy and strengthening the brain.

In the *Lin Qu: Hai Lun Pien* it is written, "The brain is the sea of marrow, when there is a surplus of marrow the body is full of energy, if there is a deficiency of marrow, there will be ringing in the ears, the legs will ache, one will be dizzy, the eyesight will not be clear and one will be unable to sleep soundly." The *Su Wen: Jie Jing Wei Lun* states, "The marrow fills the bones." In the *Wei Lun* it is also written, "When the bones are 'dry' the marrow will be insufficient, the bones will wither." These passages refer to the fact that the brain is responsible for the movement of the body and the clarity of sight. The marrow nourishes the bones. Therefore, the kidneys, brain, essence, marrow, bones and connective tissue all have a reciprocal effect on one another and are mutually supportive of the other's growth. Strengthening the meridians by rubbing the knees and stretching the body is an exercise of the Xing Yi health exercise set which stimulates and strengthens the meridians, bones, and marrow. Additionally it aids the movement capabilities of the limbs, strengthens the kidneys, benefits the brain, increases the production of essence and marrow, balances the *yin* and *yang* of the body, improves the functions of the internal organs, slows the aging process and extends life.

Preparatory Posture: Stand naturally (photo 14-1)

Method of Practice:

1. Raise the left leg and place the heel on a low stool (if one does not have access to a stool or similar object, one may extend the leg straight out in front and place the heel on the ground with the toes pointing up and the right leg slightly bent).
2. The palms are placed one on top of the other on the left knee. Rub the knee in clockwise circles for a number of repetitions then reverse the direction (photo 14-2).
3. Reach and grab the toes of the left foot with the hands and lean the upper body over, try to touch the chin to the left heel (photo 14-3). Repeat several times.
4. Cross the arms and grab the opposite elbow with the hands. Bend forward and try to touch the toes of the left foot alternately with each elbow (photos 14-4 and 14-5). Repeat several times.
5. Switch legs and repeat steps 1 - 5 (photos 14-6 through 14-9).

Number of Repetitions: Repeat with each leg two times.

Important Points:

1. Try to rub and move the kneecap as much as possible.
2. Breathe naturally.
3. Beginners and those whose physical condition is not good may not be able to perform the exercise as described. Slowly try to increase the range of motion over time. Do not try to force the stretch as it may cause injury.
4. When stretching forward and pressing the leg, move slowly, stably, and smoothly, one may hold the stretch for a period of time.

The Range of Motion and Effects: The main purpose of this exercise is to stretch the legs. The leg pressing exercise is an important method of increasing the flexibility and elasticity of the legs. This skill is a common requirement of all martial arts. Those who practice calisthenic exercises, dancers and opera performers, all use the leg press. The leg press exercise includes pressing to the front and to the side. Xing Yi Quan uses the front press variation. This exercise increases the elasticity of the leg while at the same time conditions the waist, back, knees, and the muscles along the sides of the torso.

Photo 14-1

Photo 14-2

Photo 14-3

Photo 14-4

Photo 14-5

Photo 14-6

Photo 14-7

Photo 14-8

Photo 14-9

The "Song" of Strengthening the Meridians by Rubbing the Knees and Stretching the Body

Stand naturally erect, the hands hang by the sides.
Concentrate the spirit and quiet the *qi*, close out interfering thoughts as much as possible.
The heart is calm as still water, heaven and earth exist together.
The eyes look straight ahead, the limbs and body relax.
Close the mouth, the tongue touches the roof of the mouth.
The *qi* and blood fill the arteries, moving in and out of the "sea of *qi*."

The left leg extends a step to the front.
The heel is on the ground, the toes point upward.
The hands press on the knee gently, rub the knee from left to right.

Lean the body forward, the power is in the hips.
Stretch the waist as if the head wants to touch the toes.
Twist the body, bend the left elbow and touch the toes with the left elbow.
Twist the body, bend the right elbow and touch the toes with right elbow.
Repeat as long as comfortable.

The right leg extends a step to the front.
The heel is on the ground, the toes point upward.
The hands press the knee gently, rub the knee from left to right.

Lean the body forward, the power is in the hips.
Stretch the waist as if the head wants to touch the toes.
Twist the body, bend the left elbow and touch the toes with the left elbow.
Twist the body, bend the right elbow and touch the toes with right elbow.
Repeat as long as comfortable.

Exercise Fifteen: *Yin* Opens and *Yang* Closes

Introduction: When *yin* and *yang* are balanced in the body, the internal organs will all function harmoniously, the "five elements" will change appropriately and all systems will function normally. This exercise regulates the breath, thereby stimulating and strengthening the heart, improving the functions of the gall bladder and stomach, improving digestion and the absorption of nutrients, benefiting the internal organs, improving the overall health, cultivating the spirit, increasing energy and extending life.

Preparatory Posture: Stand naturally with the feet together (photo 15-1).

Method of Practice:

1. Lift the hands up in front of the body until they are at the height of the shoulders. The arms are straight with the palms facing downward (photo 15-2).
2. The arms move outward to the left and right until they are straight out to the sides of the body in a straight line. As the arms reach the straight out position, the palms turn over to face up (photos 15-3 and 15-4).
3. Continuing, close the hands together again in front of the body, turning the hands to face palm down as they move in towards each other (photos 15-5 through 15-7).
4. Repeat the exercise, opening and closing the arms.

Number of Repetitions: Repeat the movement sixteen times.

Important Points:

1. Inhale as the hands open, exhale as the hands close.
2. The movement should be slow and gentle.
3. Be careful not to stick out the chest.

The Range of Motion and Effects: This is primarily a breathing exercise. The muscles of the chest, the intercostal muscles and the diaphragm are all conditioned. The slow and gentle movement coupled with the smooth and stable breathing also serves as a regulatory exercise which balances the body. The effects of this exercise are especially apparent if performed after the "crawling tiger" exercise (see the supplementary exercise section).

Photo 15-1

Photo 15-2

Photo 15-3

Photo 15-4

Photo 15-5

Photo 15-6

Photo 15-7

Photo 15-8

The "Song" of Yin Opens and Yang Closes

Stand naturally erect, the arms hang at the sides.
Concentrate the spirit, quiet the *qi*, close out interfering thoughts as much as possible.
The heart is calm as still water, heaven and earth exist together.
The eyes look straight ahead, the limbs and body are relaxed.
Close the mouth, the tongue touches the roof of the mouth.
The *qi* and blood fill the arteries, moving in and out of the "sea of *qi*."

The two arms are slowly raised to the front.
They come to the height of the shoulders, the palms face downward.
Move the arms out to the left and right keeping them parallel with the ground.
The arms move out until they are in a straight line to the sides.
Slowly inhale as the arms move outward.

Turn the palms to face palm up,
Move them in together to the center.
The hands move until they are together in front of the body, slowly exhale.
Repeat as long as comfortable.

Exercise Sixteen: The Heels Kick Backward

At the conclusion of any exercise set, the body should gently be brought to a calm and natural position. The energy of the body, which has been stimulated and transported throughout the body during the practice, is allowed to gather and sink to the *dan tian*. The heel kick exercise regulates the energy of the whole body and will relax the body after exercise.

Preparatory Posture: Stand naturally with the feet together (photo 16-1).

Method of Practice:

1. Bend the knee and kick backward with force, try to touch the heel to the buttocks (photo 16-2).
2. Alternate kicking back with the right and left legs (photos 16-2 and 16-3).

Number of Repetitions: One may repeat thirty six times or more.

Important Points:

1. Perform the exercise slowly and gently. Breathe naturally.
2. The arms hang naturally at the sides. Look straight ahead. While kicking the body should not sway.

The Range of Motion and Effects: This is a very old Xing Yi Quan exercise used to regulate the body. This movement will relax the whole body after exercise.

Photo 16-1

Photo 16-2a

**Photo 16-2b
(side view)**

Photo 16-3

Photo 16-4

Supplemental Exercise

The Crawling Tiger
(Laying on the Palms)

Preparatory Posture: Stand naturally

Method of Practice:

1. Make two fists and lower yourself down onto the ground in the push-up position (resting on the fists). The hands are shoulder width apart (one may also perform this exercise on the fingertips or holding onto wooden handles). Hold the arms straight, the body parallel to the ground, supported by the hands in the front and the balls of the feet in the rear (photo S-1).
2. Bend the elbows and allow the body to drop down parallel to the ground and about six inches above the ground (photo S-2).
3. Push up with the arms while the buttocks stay in place (photo S-3).
4. Look straight ahead. Concentrate the spirit, look back to the right and then to the left. The legs are together.
5. Lift the buttocks and the waist to the rear (photos S-4 and S-5).
6. Push forward with the legs down into the low push-up position (photo S-6).
7. Repeat 1 - 3 times (photos S-2 through S-6).

Number of Repetitions: Do as many your endurance permits.

Important Points:

1. Breathe naturally.

2. Do not overdo the exercise.

3. After completing the exercise, concentrate the spirit and stand up.

The Range of Motion and Effects: This exercise stimulates the entire body. The torso, extremities and head are all involved. If one's physical condition permits, one may add this exercise after exercise fourteen "Rub the Knees and Press the Legs." From the first exercise through the "crawling tiger" makes up the training section of the system. Exercises fifteen and sixteen are cool down exercises which serve to regulate and relax the body.

Photo S-1

Photo S-2

Photo S-3

Photo S-4

Photo S-5

Photo S-6

Song of the Sixteen Health Exercises
by Zhang Bao Yang

The two hands circle as if closing up.

The front hand drags, the back hand hooks and they pull diagonally with force.

The fists slowly rotate front and back over the crown of the head.

The hands clap above and below and the body stands erect.

The two hands hold up the sky and also support the heart, take a step forward and rotate the eyes.

One hand holds up the sky as the other presses the earth.

Look left, gaze right and see what is behind, the head rises and lowers with the strength of the neck.

The posture of the body looks like that of an ape.

The hand strokes, the neck turns and the body squats down, the back shakes and the foul air is expired.

The two fists strike the back as the body leans to the rear.

If the waist is rotated round and round the kidneys benefit.

Move the knees left and right with the body lowered.

Turn the knees, flex and extend while the toes grip the ground.

Kneading the knees and exercising the legs one must bend the waist.

With the *yang* of opening and the *yin* of closing the lungs are free of disease.

Kicking the rear with feet causes the *qi* to descend. These are the sixteen exercises of Xing Yi Quan.

The crawling tiger uses both hands for support.

The above song was written by Zhang Bao Yang in order to help students remember the order and important points of the exercises. It is printed here for your consideration. The crawling tiger was originally not part of the sixteen exercises, however, as we commonly practice this exercise along with the others the line about it has been added to the song.

Afterword

My classmates and I followed our fathers and have practiced martial arts with master Wang Ji Wu from six or seven years of age. Before practice, we invariably performed the sixteen exercises. Sometimes because of schoolwork, I didn't have enough time to practice Xing Yi Quan, but I never missed a day of practicing the sixteen exercises. Later, as I was growing up, I often followed Master Wang in his medical practice. As soon as a patient was near recovery, the Master would teach them the sixteen exercises. This not only speeded recovery but also helped to prevent any complications and made the body strong. After I began my career as a health practitioner, I followed Master Wang's example and taught the sixteen exercises to my patients. In order to raise the level of health of the people, and aid in the prevention of disease, we offer this set of exercises and hope that others in the health care profession may find them useful in their own professions.

Wang Huan Sheng
Beijing, Chung Wen District
Chian Men Hospital
January, 1981

Xing Yi Exercises Performed Lying On A Bed

Edited and Transmitted by Zhang Bao Yang
Translated by Tim Cartmell

Introduction:

The following exercise set is performed in the morning before getting out of bed and in the evening before going to sleep. It will help awaken the body and prepare it for the day in the morning and relax the body before sleep at night.

Exercises:

The heart and mind are quiet, the *qi* and blood are pure,

practice morning and night, the exercises lying on a bed.

Rub the hands together, until they are warm,

then "wash" (rub) the face, the blood vessels will all open.

Rub the eyes with the hands, this clears the vision,

rub beside the nose, the breathing passages will be open.

Clench the teeth together, it will strengthen the gums,

wash the mouth with air, this produces more saliva.

Comb the hair with the hands, the spirit will be pure,

rub the neck, it will dispel the effects of drafts.

Strike the "sky drum" (the base of the skull), listen to the sound,

rub the ears, the hearing will be sharp.

Rub the upper arms, this will open the meridians,

and also helps the circulation, this is a supplement to training.

Use the fists to rub the waist, thus preventing pain,

knead the hips, the joints will feel light.

Rub the lower extremities, this also opens the meridians,

push down along the outside, and return along the inside.

Rub the soles of the feet, this benefits the essence of the kidneys,

move the balls of the feet, relax the ankles.

Push on the right ribs, to soothe the liver,

move to the left ribs, the spleen and stomach will be free of obstruction.

Rub the *Shen Que* (in the middle of the upper back), with an empty palm,

pushing on the *Ren* meridian, the "triple warmer" will be clear.

After a long period of practice, disease will not be able to take hold,

be consistent in practice, do not take these exercises lightly.

Our ancestors passed this knowledge down, it is a marvelous method,

to be preserved for future generations, to save the ill.

Wang Ji Wu executing Xing Yi's Pao Quan

Chapter 6

Xing Yi Five Element Spear

Zhang Bao Yang with the Xing Yi "Needles"

Xing Yi Five Element Spear
by Dan Miller

Introduction

All systems of Chinese internal martial arts include some type of power development training using heavy and/or long weapons. Tai Ji practitioners utilize a long spear or staff, Ba Gua practitioners use a large broadsword, large straight sword, and a long spear, and Xing Yi practitioners utilize the long spear or heavy straight sword. In this chapter we will present the five Xing Yi long spear exercises which are associated with the five element fist movements of the Xing Yi open hand system.

Typically the Xing Yi student will not be taught the five element long spear practice until he or she has spent a considerable amount of time practicing the *san ti* standing practice and the bare hand forms. If the body's alignments and the movements and mechanics of the bare hand forms are not correct, when the student practices with the spear, these bad habits will be further ingrained as the student will be trying to "muscle" the spear with his arms and upper body instead of using aligned strength and whole body power. On the other hand, if the student has spent a sufficient amount of time with the bare hand forms and his or her mechanics and power are correct, practice of the five element long spear exercises will greatly enhance the student's practice.

Each of the spear techniques will improve the whole body connection and power necessary for performance of the five fists. Although the hand and arm movements are not exactly the same in some cases, it is the power coming from the legs and torso that these spear techniques are training. After the student has practiced these spear methods, there should be a noticeable difference in the execution of the bare hand methods. The spear that is used is approximately 10 to 12 feet in length, however, smaller spears can be used. In fact, beginning students may want to start with a six foot spear until the mechanics of the movement are correct before trying to use a longer, heavier spear.

Note: The photographs taken in this section were captured from a video that was taken by one of Zhang Bao Yang's students. The original video was taken on a home video camera in the PAL format used in mainland China. This video had to be converted to the NTSC format used in the United States and thus some of the resolution was lost in the conversion process. Due to the conversion and video capture, the photos are not quite as clear as we would like them to be, however, we feel that they are clear enough for the reader to understand the movements and since this was the only source of photographs available we went ahead and used them.

In all photograph sequences the sequence begins in the middle of a repetitive line. Because of the camera angle and the distance from the camera when Zhang began the line, the photographs of the beginning and ending form were not clear enough to include here. However, the form beginning and ending are inconsequential.

Pi Qiang (劈槍 - Splitting Spear)

The splitting spear movements train the mechanics of the downward (vertical) striking motion of the splitting fist. Concentration should be focused on expanding the torso (especially the intercostal muscles) as the spear moves upward and the contracting of the torso as the spear moves downward. See the photographs on the following page.

Photo 1: In this photo Zhang has just completed one repetition and is about to begin another. Begin in the *san ti* stance with the spear held approximately level to the ground.

Photo 2: Step forward with the rear leg and begin to pull the spear straight upward. As you pull the spear upward, do not use the arm, use the torso to move the spear. The arm will remain in an almost straight position throughout the execution of this movement. The forward hand slides up the shaft of the spear as the spear moves upward. Do not grip the spear with the forward hand and pull upward with the arm. Allow the hand to slide as the back muscles move the weapon.

Photo 3: Raise the forward knee up so that the thigh is parallel to the ground as you continue to bring the spear straight up to a perfectly vertical position. The forward hand continues to slide up the shaft of the spear as the spear is lifted. The forward arm is straight and vertical in this position and the chest is expanded on the forward hand side. However, the shoulders are relaxed.

Photo 4: Step out with the forward leg and begin to press the spear straight downward. Use a contracting motion in the chest, torso, and back, however do not allow the chest to collapse or the back to round. The spine remains straight. The contracting motion is straight downward. Do not press down with the arm muscles. Allow the psoas muscle, the intercostal muscles and the latisimus dorsi muscles to do the work. The hand of the forward arm will slide inward along the spear shaft as the arm moves downward.

Photo 5: The forward foot is planted on the ground as the spear continues to split downward. Again, the hand is sliding along the shaft. Do not push downward with the arm. Allow the sliding of the hand to press the spear downward.

Photo 6: The spear has split all the way down to a level parallel to the ground. The momentum of the downward motion will carry the tip lower than parallel, however, you want to stop the downward motion of your arms at the parallel position. Begin to bring the rear leg forward and execute the next repetition.

Splitting Spear 1

Splitting Spear 2

Splitting Spear 3

Splitting Spear 4

Splitting Spear 5

Splitting Spear 6

Zuan Qiang (鑽槍 - Drilling Spear)

The drilling spear movement is very similar to both the basic Tai Ji and the Ba Gua long spear power exercises. As in all of the spear exercises, the practitioner should concentrate on the movements of the torso and not muscle the spear with the arms and shoulders. All movements should be smooth and fluid.

Photo 1: Start in a *san ti* stance with the spear straight out in front of you. In this photo Zhang has just completed one repetition and is getting ready for the next so the spear is held a bit higher in this picture than in the normal starting posture.

Photo 2: Pull the spear back with the rear hand allowing the spear shaft to slide through the front hand (front hand stays in place). This movement is executed by expanding from the center of the body and opening up in the chest area, however do not stick out the chest too far. Do not simply draw the arm back without the movement being initiated from the center of the body. All movements come from the center of the body and torso, not the arms alone. As the spear is drawn back, begin to step forward with the rear foot into a forward cross-step position. Also, as the spear is drawn back, the front hand turns over to face palm up.

Photo 3: After the spear is drawn back to the position shown in photo 2, the rear hand flips up towards the rear shoulder and there is a quick flicking motion of the rear wrist. The rear elbow stays in place as the hand moves toward the shoulder. The motion of the rear forearm and wrist should cause the spear tip to move downward and to the left side. The stepping foot continues forward.

Photo 4: With the elbow still in place, the rear forearm rotates away from the body and downward. This will bring the spear tip back up to center. The stepping foot begins to plant firmly on the ground.

Photo 5: The rear hand continues moving downward and begins to move in towards the body as the elbow moves outward slightly (notice the difference in the rear elbow position between photos 4 and 5).

Photo 6: When the forward foot is planted on the ground the body weight shifts forward and the forward hand rotates and presses downward on the spear shaft. Notice that in photo 5 the forward hand is facing upward and in photo 6 it is facing downward. The overturning of the palm helps whip the spear downward and to the right. In the sequence starting in photo 3 and ending with photo 6, the spear tip has drawn a horseshoe shaped pattern in the air. It moved downward and to the left in photo 3, upward to center in photos 4 and 5, and then downward and to the right in photo 6. The flicking upward of the wrist (in photo 3) and the rolling over of the palm (in photo 6) help the spear move properly.

Photo 7: The rear foot begins to step forward and the rear hand begins to push the spear shaft straight forward.

Photo 8: The rear foot continues stepping forward and the rear hand continues pushing the spear shaft straight forward. The spear shaft slides through the forward hand as it is thrust straight forward.

Photo 9: The rear foot steps forward as the spear is thrust forward.

Photo 10: The rear hand meets the front hand as the stepping foot is planted firmly on the ground and the arms extend in a full forward thrust of the spear. The practitioner is now ready to repeat the movements.

Drilling Spear 1

Drilling Spear 2

Drilling Spear 3

Drilling Spear 4

Drilling Spear 5

Drilling Spear 6

Drilling Spear 7

Drilling Spear 8

Drilling Spear 9

Drilling Spear 10

Beng Qiang (崩槍 - Smashing Spear)

The smashing spear movements are almost identical to the movements of the open hand smashing fist as executed in Wang Ji Wu's Xing Yi system. The motion of the hips and torso rotating around the body's center helps to provide the power in this movement.

Photo 1: Begin in a *san ti* posture with the spear straight forward and level.

Photo 2: Step forward with the forward leg, turn at the hips so that the forward hip moves forward. The forward shoulder moves forward in coordination with the step and hip movement and the forward hand slides forward on the spear shaft and presses downward slightly with a quick, crisp motion. The spear tip should move downward as shown in the photo. The movement of the forward hand is coordinated with the movement of the forward step.

Photo 3: The weight moves forward and the rear leg begins to step forward.

Photo 4: The rear leg continues to step forward as the rear hand begins pushing the spear forward. The spear shaft moves through the forward hand.

Photo 5: As the rear foot is planted just behind the forward foot, the spear is thrust forward with the rear hand. The two hands meet together as the spear is thrust forward. Do not execute this movement by simply pushing with the arm. The rotation of the rear hip forward and the coordinated movement of the hip and shoulder in conjunction with the step provide the thrusting force.

Photo 6: Begin to step forward with the forward leg and draw the spear back with the rear hand.

Photo 7: Continue stepping forward and drawing the spear back. The spear shaft slides through the forward hand.

Photo 8: Repeat as explained in step 2 above.

Smashing Spear 1   **Smashing Spear 2**

Smashing Spear 3

Smashing Spear 4

Smashing Spear 5

Smashing Spear 6

Smashing Spear 7

Smashing Spear 8

Pao Qiang (炮槍 - Pounding Spear)

Photo 1: Start in the *san ti* posture with the spear held approximately level to the ground. The hands are held closer together in this exercise, they are approximately one foot apart on the spear shaft.

Photo 2: The rear hand rotates upward and moves up the center line of the body as the forward hand rotates downward and the arm extends straight out.

Photo 3: Begin to pull the spear back with both hands as you begin to step forward with the back leg in a forward cross-step.

Photo 4: Continue stepping forward with the rear leg and pulling the spear back with both hands. The forward palm is facing you and the rear palm is facing away from you.

Photo 5: As the rear foot hits the ground the hands are brought up to shoulder height.

Photo 6: Begin to step forward with the rear foot and bring the hands down and forward.

Photo 7: Repeat as described in step 2.

Pounding Spear 1

Pounding Spear 2

Pounding Spear 3

Pounding Spear 4

Pounding Spear 5

Pounding Spear 6

Pounding Spear 7

Heng Qiang (橫槍 - Crossing Spear)

Photo 1: Start in the *san ti* stance with the spear parallel to the ground.

Photo 2: Pull across the front of your body to the left with the forward hand. Insure that the movement comes from the torso, not the arm. The forward hand slides forward on the spear shaft as you pull.

Photo 3: Push the spear back across the front of the body as you begin to execute a forward cross-step with the rear foot.

Photo 4: Continue executing the forward cross-step and push the spear across the front of the body horizontally. The spear shaft remains parallel to the ground. The forward hand slides on the spear shaft as it pushes. Do not push from the arm muscles, use the turning motion of the hips and shoulders.

Photo 5: The rear foot lands forward as the spear reaches the limit of its crossing movement to the right.

Photo 6: Begin stepping forward with the rear leg and pulling the spear back across the body to the left. The forward arm remains relatively straight and slides on the spear shaft as the movement of the torso pulls the spear across the front of the body. Do not pull the spear with the arm alone, allow the hips to do the work.

Photo 7: Continue stepping forward with the rear foot and pulling the spear across the front of the body.

Photo 8: Repeat as specified above in step 2.

Crossing Spear 1

Crossing Spear 2

Crossing Spear 3

Crossing Spear 4

Crossing Spear 5

Crossing Spear 6

Crossing Spear 7

Crossing Spear 8

Zhang Bao Yang with the Xing Yi Short Staff

About the Translator

Tim Cartmell

Tim Cartmell began his martial arts training in Kung Fu San Soo in 1972 at the age of eleven. He received his eighth degree black belt (Master's Degree) in the art in 1984.

After graduation from Long Beach State University in 1984, Tim moved to the Republic of China (Taiwan) to begin training in the internal Chinese martial arts. Originally studying with Master Hsu Hong Chi, Tim earned his black belt in Tang Shou Tao Xing Yi in 1987.

In 1986, Tim won the middleweight division of the All Taiwan Invitational Full Contact Tournament and again won that division of the Chung Cheng International Full Contact Tournament later that same year. Tim has studied Ba Gua Zhang, Xing Yi Quan, Chen and Yang style Tai Ji Quan, Yi Quan, the White Crane system, and various other methods of Qi Gong and internal boxing since moving to Taiwan. He is presently a senior student of Ba Gua Zhang Master Luo De Xiu. In addition to his martial arts training, Tim studied Chinese language and literature full time at the Taiwan Normal University for five years. Tim Cartmell still lives in the Republic of China where he practices and teaches martial arts, writes, and works as a translator.

Wang Jin Yu, Zhang Bao Yang, and Tim Cartmell

About the Editor

Dan Miller

A native of Springfield, Virginia, Dan Miller graduated from the United States Naval Academy in Annapolis, Maryland in 1982 with a Bachelor of Science in Mathematics and accepted a commission in the United States Marine Corps. He subsequently served for ten years as an officer of Marines. While in the military he was sent to study at the Naval Postgraduate School in Monterey, California (1987-1989) and earned a Masters Degree in Electrical Engineering.

Dan began his study of Chinese martial arts and Qi Gong in 1983. Since that time he has studied Ba Gua Zhang, Xing Yi Quan, Tai Ji Quan and Qi Gong with various instructors in the United States, Taiwan, and mainland China. He currently studies Ba Gua Zhang with Park Bok Nam and Xing Yi Quan with Vince Black.

In 1990, Dan and his wife Nancy founded High View Publications and began publishing the *Pa Kua Chang Newsletter*. In 1992 the newsletter was upgraded to a Journal and Dan Miller left the military service to pursue martial arts practice, publishing, and instructing full time. Since moving back to the Monterey Peninsula in the fall of 1992 Dan Miller has taught Ba Gua Zhang, Tai Ji Quan and Xing Yi Quan, continued to edit and publish the *Pa Kua Chang Journal*, has published five martial arts books and produced three martial arts instructional videos.

Wang Jin Yu, Zhang Bao Yang, and Dan Miller

High View Publications
P.O. Box 51967
Pacific Grove, CA 93950
Phone: (408) 655-2990
Fax: (408) 655-4984

High View Publications specializes in publishing books pertaining to all areas of Chinese Health and Fitness including martial arts, Qi Gong, medicine, philosophy and religion. Please write to the address above for our current catlog.

Xing Yi Nei Gong
Xing Yi Health Maintenance and
Internal Strength Development

形意

内功

compiled and edited by
Dan Miller and Tim Cartmell

Xing Yi Nei Gong
Xing Yi Health Maintenance and
Internal Strength Development

Over 200 pages, 7 X 10 format, includes:
• Xing Yi History and Lineage going back 8 generations.
• Xing Yi *Written Transmissions* taken from hand-copied manuscripts handed down from 3rd and 4th generation practitioners Dai Long Bang and Li Neng Ran.
• Sixteen Xing Yi Health Maintenance and Power Development Exercises handed down by the famous Xing Yi master Wang Ji Wu (1891 - 1991) described in detail and shown in clear, easy-to-follow photographs taken of Wang Ji Wu's disciple Zhang Bao Yang (1922 -).
• Xing Yi Qi Gong Exercises handed down by master Wang Ji Wu.
• Xing Yi's *San Ti Shi* standing practice and theory described in great detail with accompanying photographs of both Wang Ji Wu and Zhang Bao Yang.
• Xing Yi Five Element Long Spear power training exercises demonstrated by Zhang Bao Yang.

$19.95
(Plus Shipping & Handling)

Book and Video

The Fundamentals of
Pa Kua Chang

The Method of Lu Shui-T'ien as Taught by Park Bok Nam
by Park Bok Nam and Dan Miller

Book: $19.95
Video: $49.95
Book & Video: $65.00
Plus Shipping and Handling

The Fundamentals of Pa Kua Chang
The method of Lu Shui-T'ien as
Taught by Park Bok Nam

All Martial Artists can now easily learn to develop the skills which made the Pa Kua Chang fighters famous in China:

- **Highly Evasive Footwork**
- **Powerful Palm Strikes**
- **Snake-Like Body Movements**
- **Lightning-Fast Combinations**
- **Ch'i Kung**
- **Health and Longevity**

In this new book and companion video Park Bok Nam describes in detail and demonstrates the various components of Pa Kua Chang's basic training as it was taught to him by Lu Shui-T'ien. This book details exercises which will help any martial artist improve his or her footwork, body flexibility, ch'i circulation, and internal striking power.

In the 53-minute VHS video tape, Park Bok Nam demonstrates the majority of the exercises which are described in detail in the book.

You can now order by Phone or Fax:
Phone: (408) 655-2990
Fax: (408) 655-4984

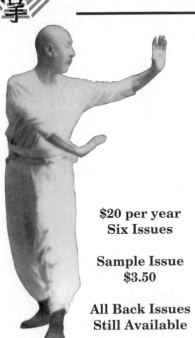

Order Form

	Qty	Unit Price	Total
Practical Chin Na		$17.95	
The Fundamentals of Pa Kua Chang (Book only)		$19.95	
The Fundamentals of Pa Kua Chang (Tape only)		$49.95	
The Fundamentals of Pa Kua Chang Book and Tape		$65.00	
Liang Zhen Pu Eight Diagram Palm		$17.95	
Tru-Balance Dynamics Tape		$39.95	
Pa Kua Chang Journal (one year)		$20.00	
Xing Yi Nei Gong		$19.95	
The Study of Form Mind Boxing		$19.95	
The Principles of Ba Gua Fighting (video)		$49.95	
Gao Style Ba Gua Zhang (video)		$49.95	
Pa Kua Chang T-shirt Large, X-Large (circle one)		$12.00	
Pa Kua Chang T-shirt XX-Large		$15.00	
The Honor of Dong Fang Xu (video)		$34.95	
Gong Bao Tian Style Videos 1, 2, 3, 4 (circle one)		$25.00	
Gong Bao Tian Style Videos (complete set)		$90.00	

VISA **MasterCard**

Shipping & Handling:
Add $3.50 for the first item, $1.00 per additional item

California residents add 7.25% Sales Tax:

Name: _____

Order TOTAL =

Adress: _____

City: _____ **State:** ____ **Zip:** _____

Please make check or money order payable to:
High View Publications

You can now order by Phone or Fax:
Phone: **(408) 655-2990**
Fax: **(408) 655-4984**

# NORTH AMERICAN TANG SHOU TAO

Individuals wishing to find out more about the art of Xing Yi Quan, or locate a Xing Yi instructor, should contact the North American Tang Shou Tao Association. North American Tang Shou Tao is the largest Xing Yi Quan association in North America with member schools and qualified instructors located throughout the United States.

In addition to its yearly full-contact Xing Yi Quan tournament and instructors conferences, North American Tang Shou Tao periodically sponsors teams to compete in full-contact tournaments in Taiwan, sponsors qualified instructors from Taiwan and Mainland China for seminar tours of the United States, and sponsors intensive group study trips in mainland China.

North American Tang Shou Tao is associated with the International Tang Shou Tao Association based in Taipei, Taiwan. Write to:

North American Tang Shou Tao
P. O. Box 36235
Tucson, AZ 85740